A guide to being YOU

Sharon Witt

Girl Wise* – A girl's guide to being you
Copyright © 2013 Sharon Witt

20 19 18 17 16 15 14 7 6 5 4 3 2 1

First published 2013 by Collective Wisdom Publications.
This edition published 2014 by Authentic Media Ltd
52, Presley Way, Crownhill, Milton Keynes, MK8 0ES.

www.authenticmedia.co.uk

British Library Cataloguing in Publication Data
A catalogue record for this book is available from the British Library

ISBN-13: 978-1-86024-914-3

Design and cartoons: Ivan Smith, Communiqué Graphics, Lilydale, Australia.
Printed in Great Britain by Bell and Bain, Glasgow.

This book belongs
to an amazing girl

Abigail Anna
Docherty

You are a wonderful, creative, inspiring,

cherished girl

You are a SHINING STAR!

Inside...

Hi there!

Welcome to Girl Wise – a series of books that have been created especially for **YOU.**

Why? Because you are an **INCREDIBLE** and AMAZING girl and sometimes you just might need a little bit of encouragement along the way and to be reminded just how beautiful and capable you are.

Sometimes, when we are younger, we go through some wonderful times, but also some tough times too. Whether you are having problems with friends, are worrying about how you look or just feeling a bit down in the dumps – this book is written especially for YOU.

I hope you enjoy reading it and just know that you are **NEVER** alone.

You are AMAZING! ☺

Love Sharon

YOU ARE UNIQUE AND VALUABLE

You are an Amazing Girl!

You are an amazing girl. Yes, **YOU!**

You are capable of so very much that you can probably not even begin to imagine right now.

When you were first born, you had the entire world at your feet.

No matter where you live or where you come from, you can dream up amazing things to do and **BE.**

You have been created truly unique and valuable.

There has never been – and will never be – another **YOU** in this world.

That makes **YOU** very **SPECIAL!**

'Always be a first-rate version of yourself
instead of a second-rate version of someone else.'

Judy Garland

You have been created truly unique and valuable

'I praise you because I am fearfully and wonderfully made; your works are wonderful, I know that full well.'

Psalm 139:14 (NIV)

Have you ever walked along a beach that was covered in shells?

Have you ever just stopped and spent hours looking at all the different shapes and sizes?

Have you ever created your own shell collection?

Why would you collect something as simple as shells? Because there is **NEVER EVER** a single shell that is **EXACTLY** the SAME as another.

Some have been washed up after many years in the ocean, while others have had small sea creatures living in them for a while.

They are simply amazing and each and every single one is different.

You can find shells that are spiky, some that are smooth, some that are different colours, and others that look like they are covered in glistening pearls. Some are so smooth it seems like they have been washed in the ocean for hundreds of years.

You, my dear girl, are very much like one of those precious sea shells. You have been created as a truly unique and special girl by God, who simply **ADORES** you. You may get some lumps and bumps along the way. You may have scars, both on the inside and the outside, but that makes you more and more precious to those who find you and grow to love YOU!

Just like the precious seashells — and there are MILLIONS of them all over the world — someone will still pick one up from the sandy shore and say, 'YOU are special. You are unique. I will place you somewhere special.'

You are cherished!

'God pays even greater attention to you, down to the last detail — even numbering the hairs on your head!'
Luke 12:7 (MSG)

Have you ever collected **SEASHELLS**?

Next time you go to the beach, look for that **SPECIAL** and **RARE** shell that will remind you that you too are **UNIQUE.**

'You are the only YOU God made... God made you and broke the mould.'

Max Lucado

'Whatever you are, be a good one.'

Abraham Lincoln

'Comparison is the thief of joy.'

Unknown

YOU are exactly WHO and WHAT and WHERE YOU are supposed to be And YOU are lovely! (anything else would be just plain ridiculous)

How do others describe you?

If your friends, teachers and family were asked to describe YOU, what sort of words do you think they might use?

List these here...

....

....

....

....

....

Words I would use to describe me are...

....

....

....

....

....

Qualities...

friendly	quiet	humorous
reserved	**happy**	**thoughtful**
caring	creative	bright
bubbly	talkative	**helpful**
organised	observant	musical
strong	**loving**	studious
gentle	punctual	careful
energetic	**sporty**	**knowing**
loud	godly	sensitive
beautiful	**unselfish**	generous
inspiring	optimistic	**forgiving**
courageous	confident	imaginative
talented	**responsible**	thankful
compassionate	enthusiastic	capable

Don't compare yourself

'To be yourself in a world that is constantly trying to make you something else is the greatest achievement.'

Ralph Waldo Emerson

When we are growing up, sometimes we might start to COMPARE ourselves to the friends around us. I remember thinking popular people had to look and act a certain way when I was younger.

I thought that you needed to be tall, slim, have blonde hair and blue eyes in order to be seen as popular and

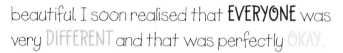

beautiful. I soon realised that **EVERYONE** was very DIFFERENT and that was perfectly OKAY.

So what if I was short and had brown hair that had funny curls?

These physical qualities were what made me **UNIQUE** and **ME***!*

What mattered even more was who I was on the INSIDE*!*

I could be very friendly, I had a wonderful smile and I always looked for the very best in people that I met.

I soon realised that comparing myself to others was NOT WORTH the energy it took up. I was never going to be exactly like anyone else!

Sure, we could dress the same or wear our hair in the same style, but we would always be a copy of someone else.

And just imagine what a boring world it would be if we were all created **EXACTLY** the **SAME**.

'Be yourself;
everyone else is already taken.'
Oscar Wilde

I have amazing potential.
    I can make good choices.
I am never alone.
    I can do hard things.
I am beautiful
    inside and out.
I am of great worth.
    He has a plan for me.
I know who I am –
    a daughter of God.

Unknown

YOUR GIFTS AND TALENTS

Your gifts and talents

'Use what talents you possess.
The woods would be very silent if
no birds sang except
those that sang best.'

Henry Van Dyke

Have you ever received a birthday present or special gift but had **NO IDEA** what was inside the wrapping? Perhaps the gift was wrapped in brightly coloured or shiny balloon-patterned paper. Perhaps it was inside a large or small box, just to disguise what the gift might be.

It is **VERY EXCITING** to receive a special gift, isn't it! My favourite thing is to GIVE GIFTS to other people. I LOVE to see their faces when they see that something was bought or made JUST FOR THEM. For me, it is much more fun watching SOMEONE UNWRAP A GIFT, THAN IT IS TO RECEIVE A PRESENT.

Finding out what you are good at —
your gifts and talents — is a bit like
unwrapping an amazing gift. You may
not realise that you have a wonderful
singing voice until you try singing. Then
you might really surprise yourself when
people begin telling you how sweet you
sound. That is a **GIFT!**

I am unique

What makes me unique and different is:

I am –
- great at encouraging others,
- a fabulous runner,
- great at caring for others,
- adventurous,
- awesome at talking to others,
- **WONDERFUL** at creating things.

That's what makes me **ME!**

Isaballe D

I am special

Everyone is **SPECIAL** in God's eyes but I am special because I have a great sense of humour.

I'm good at sport.

I like drawing and I'm excellent at Maths.

PS – I'm great at making up words!

Jade L

Everyone is special in their own way

But these are the reasons why I am special:

I'm talented at drawing

I have a funny laugh

I'm short

I like the way God made me.

I'm creative

I'm **SPECIAL** the way I am.

So that's what makes me me!

Janiq

I am special because...

God gave me a talent for reading and writing.

I am **SPECIAL** because I am good at encouraging others.

God has given every single person a talent.

But this is why I am special in God's eyes.

Grace

How do I find out what MY gifts and talents are?

That's the **FUN** part!

God has given each of us amazing strengths. Sometimes it might take you a while before you find out what your own gifts and talents are, but YOU definitely DO have talents. Half the fun is trying **NEW** and DIFFERENT things until you find some that you **ENJOY** doing.

I didn't discover how much I loved writing until I was much older. Then, it was even more exciting to discover something I was good at AND enjoyed doing.

When I was a younger girl, I would try out many different activities to see if I liked them or if I was any good at them.

I tried singing but I found out before long that I didn't really enjoy it all that much.

I found that I **LOVED** making cards and objects out of crafts and stickers. Before long, I would sell the cards I made to friends and family.

The thing to remember is, you might try MANY DIFFERENT sports, crafts and activities before you find what you enjoy the most.

If you find it BORING and **TIRING**, maybe it is not the thing for you. Move on and try something else.

Also remember, sometimes you'll find things you are good at that also take lots of time and practice!

'The person born with a talent they are meant to use, will find their greatest happiness in using it.'

Johann von Goethe

Try some of these...

sewing ✗	knitting ✓	fishing ✓
surfing ✗	craft ✓	writing ✓
singing ✓	acting ✓	bike riding ✓
ballet ✓	gymnastics ✓	acrobatics ✗
running ✓	tennis ✓	hockey ✗
cricket ✗	basketball ✗	netball ✗
ice skating ✓	roller-skating ✓	dancing ✓
swimming ✓	football ✓	baseball ✗
building —	debating —	go-karting ✓
rugby ✗	song writing —	cooking ✓
drawing ✓	painting ✓	guitar ✓
piano ✓	violin ✗	cello ✗
drums ✓	bass guitar —	trumpet ✓
flute —	skiing ✗	hiking ✓

Make a list of the things you have tried before:

....

....

....

....

....

Make a list here of the things you would like to try:

....

....

....

....

....

Everyone is special!

Everyone is special in God's eyes,

But the things that make ME special are...

I have a **HEART** for others

I am a good PROBLEM SOLVER

I ENCOURAGE others

I am ORGANISED

I am **CREATIVE**

I am awesome at **TALKING** to others

And I am great at HAIR STYLES

by Sienna Charalambous

Individuality rules!

There is greatness in YOU –
in all that you do,
all that you say,
and in the way you
are a million times
every day.

Be happy.
Be bold.
Be intelligent.
Be energetic.
Be understanding.
Be colourful.
Be creative...

In other words: just BE YOU!

By Ashley Rice

Has anyone told you lately
      how incredible you are?

No one does YOU quite like YOU DO!

You are the BEST EVER person at being you.

No one else can or will ever be YOU!

That should make you feel really special indeed.

And it also lets you off the hook —
      it means that you don't have to try and
      be anything or anyone that you are NOT.

Sharon Witt

'If everyone lit their own candle,
the whole world would be lit.'

Mary Moskovitz

'Shoot for the moon.
Even if you miss,
you'll land among the stars.'

Les Brown

'Oh yes, you shaped me first inside,
   then out;
you formed me in my mother's womb.
I thank you, High God
   – you're breathtaking!
Body and soul, I am marvellously made!
   I worship in adoration
      – what a creation!
You know me inside and out,
   you know every bone in my body;
You know exactly how I was made,
   bit by bit,
how I was sculpted from nothing
   into something.
Like an open book, you watched me grow
   from conception to birth;
all the stages of my life
   were spread out before you,
The days of my life all prepared
   before I'd even lived one day.'

Psalm 139:13-16 (MSG)

Trying to stand out as an original

When I was in my first year of primary school, aged just 5 years old, a nurse came to the school to test our eyes and see if we needed glasses.

GLASSES!

'Now THAT would make me look DIFFERENT and ORIGINAL' I thought to myself.

So when it came to my turn to read all of the letters on the big sign, I deliberately called out different letters so that the nurse would surely think I could not see properly and would need to be kitted out for some brand new glasses immediately.

As it turned out, the nurse must have sensed something was up and nothing further happened!

That is, until many years later when I began having trouble seeing the board in my classroom. I ended up needing to wear glasses full time – which is a pain! ☺

Maybe better as a blonde?

In my secondary school years, I began to get a little bored with my mousy brown hair. It was **BORING** in my mind.

So I decided that I might look really cool as a blonde. (Well, at least a much lighter version of my boring brown hair.)

So I bought a bottle of spray solution that promised to make my hair lighter 'one shade at a time'.

One spray and a few hours in the sun would make my hair turn gradually lighter. And if you used a hairdryer on your hair, the process sped up even further!

So away I sprayed and away I dried. Before long, I could see the results before my eyes. After about a week, my hair was looking different all right. It was turning... err... *ORANGEY BLONDE!*

Yep, you guessed it! My mousy brown hair was never going to turn blonde. It was a shade of orangey/browny/blonde.

It looked **HORRIBLE!**

The more I tried to look different from who I was created to be – trying everything to disguise the BORING ME I saw in the mirror – the more I was messing up the girl I was created to be.

There is nothing wrong at all with changing your hairstyle occasionally – changing your look or style every now and then – but remember that YOU ARE AN ORIGINAL!

You don't need sprays and potions to change yourself!

'Let's just go ahead and be what we were made to be, without enviously or pridefully comparing ourselves with each other, or trying to be something we aren't.'

Romans 12:6 (MSG)

When she looks in the mirror

When she looks in the mirror
She sees a girl changing:
A girl who has a great chance
To change her life as well;
Chances to let her colours burst out
And show how bright and amazing she really is.

When she looks in the mirror
She sees someone
Who in the past might have been hiding something...
Her true self!

Every day this girl would look in the mirror
And see only negative things about herself.
Every day she pretended to be someone she wasn't,
Trying to be noticed and popular.

Then one day this girl looked in the mirror
And saw her true self
Laughing and having a great time.
And so the next morning she let her colours show,
And funnily enough
She came back from school that day
With nothing but positive thoughts.

Taylor, aged 13

SELF-ESTEEM MATTERS

Self-esteem matters

Your self-esteem refers to personal feelings of self-worth or the esteem we give ourselves.

It's a GOOD thing. In fact, a healthy self-esteem is something we can all work on. It does not mean that you think you are better than everyone else or that you are SUPERIOR. It simply means you understand that you have been created as a wonderful and amazing girl and you are VALUED for WHO YOU ARE, as an amazing creation of God.

Having a healthy self-esteem means you know you are loved, have amazing gifts and talents and enough self-belief and self-worth stored up for those difficult times that we all go through. It's like having a BUFFER.

'The best accessory a girl can have is confidence.'

Unknown

What is a BUFFER?

Imagine your self-esteem is like a giant ATM (Automatic Teller Machine).

When you're older, you must put regular deposits of money into your bank account. Otherwise, you simply won't have money there when you want to withdraw some to buy something.

Well our self-esteem can be a bit like that. We have to make sure we continually put little deposits in our self-esteem 'back account'.

For example, you might see a friend drop all of her books on the ground at school. You might bend down and pick them all up for her. Doing something for SOMEONE ELSE, without expecting anything in return, actually makes a deposit into your own self-esteem bank account.

Or perhaps you work very hard on a class assignment and put a lot of extra effort into the presentation of your work. You get it back from the teacher and she has congratulated you on a fantastic effort – that's another deposit!

Self-esteem deposits

Things you can do to make deposits
into **YOUR** self-esteem account.

DEPOSIT: Offer to help clean the house.

DEPOSIT: Offer to help out younger children in crèche or at Sunday school.

DEPOSIT: Clean out your wardrobe of clothes you've grown out of - take the clothes to a charity shop.

DEPOSIT: Offer to play with a young neighbour/ baby for a couple of hours to give a mum a break.

DEPOSIT: Make some handmade cards and write to friends or relatives you haven't seen in ages, telling them how much they mean to you.

DEPOSIT: Make a special breakfast for your family at the weekend. (Don't forget to ask a parent for help if you want to prepare anything cooked. ☺) Make the table look really pretty.

ATM IN

DEPOSIT: Unpack the dishwasher without being asked.

DEPOSIT: Tidy your room and put things in order.

DEPOSIT: Weed the garden to make it look better.

DEPOSIT: Make some bracelets to sell at school or church to raise money for a cause you feel strongly about.

DEPOSIT: Make some sweet treats for your family to enjoy.

DEPOSIT: Pick some flowers from your garden and make a bouquet for your mum or other special lady.

DEPOSIT: Write 'I love you' notes to every member of your family and put them under their pillows to find when they go to bed.

DEPOSIT: Make someone a handmade gift, wrap it and present it to them – just because. ☺

DEPOSIT: Write a song.

Why being YOU matters

In the Bible, there is a fantastic passage that talks about the body being made up of many parts.

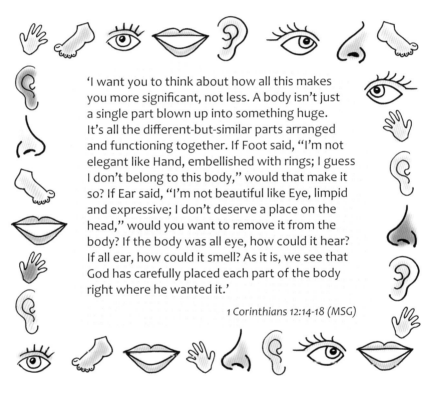

'I want you to think about how all this makes you more significant, not less. A body isn't just a single part blown up into something huge. It's all the different-but-similar parts arranged and functioning together. If Foot said, "I'm not elegant like Hand, embellished with rings; I guess I don't belong to this body," would that make it so? If Ear said, "I'm not beautiful like Eye, limpid and expressive; I don't deserve a place on the head," would you want to remove it from the body? If the body was all eye, how could it hear? If all ear, how could it smell? As it is, we see that God has carefully placed each part of the body right where he wanted it.'

1 Corinthians 12:14-18 (MSG)

This verse talks about the importance of each and every part of our bodies. Our own bodies are **AMAZING**, and are made up of many parts – including legs, arms, eyes, heart, lungs and even a liver – just to name a few.

But did you know that if just **ONE** of those parts stops working properly, you will probably know ALL about it?

For example, if you have one ear that is blocked for some reason and sounds are all muffled, you probably won't feel very well. You might feel very FRUSTRATED that you can't hear everything clearly, and you may even feel dizzy, because our ears help with balance.

Or maybe you have a broken arm or leg (**OUCH!**). It is not only very SORE, but you will probably spend several weeks unable to use your limb. You might also have other parts of your body that ACHE because they will carry a bigger load and do more work to support your broken bone.

You see, our bodies are **COMPLEX** – and have been created as incredible **MIRACLES**, where ALL PARTS are DEPENDENT on each other.

FOR SALE

Do I really matter?

Sometimes, you might feel a little left out in your class at school, your sports team or even your **FAMILY.**

But if you were missing, there would be a **GIGANTIC HOLE** where YOU should be.

It would be noticeable because YOU **MATTER!**

YOU have a part to play.

YOU bring your own unique gifts, personality, talents and style.

YOU are UNIQUE!

YOU are noticed!

YOU are loved!

What you can do if you are feeling unwanted or left out

Even though, deep down, you probably **KNOW** that you are an AMAZING and IMPORTANT part of your family, class at school, sports team, drama group or choir, there may be times when you don't feel very HAPPY or **INCLUDED**.

You might feel UNLOVED, **UNIMPORTANT** or IGNORED.

It's not a nice feeling.

It will make you feel **SAD**, UNHAPPY, SCARED or just plain **MISERABLE**.

You might not feel much like hanging out with your classmates, friends or family when you are feeling this way.

At those times, try talking with someone close who you trust. They will want to listen to you, and will want to help. They may be your mum, dad, sister, aunt or one of your closest friends.

Sometimes it really helps to talk with someone older than you, even if you think they will not have the answers you need. Sometimes just TALKING through your problems and feelings can help. And sometimes another person, especially an adult, can help give you some **PERSPECTIVE**.

'What does **PERSPECTIVE** mean?' I hear you ask.

It means seeing more than what's just in front of us.

For example, you can be so upset or bothered by a particular situation, that you can NOT see how it can get better or how it can change. Another person can help you see a way through it, or offer suggestions to help you cope. This is called getting things into **PERSPECTIVE**.

Feeling left out

I try my best every day before I head to school to put a huge smile on my face, but it soon disappears within minutes of getting to school.

I can't be myself, because I am worried that if I show my real me I would feel more rejected and not accepted.

I feel I don't fit in, coz of my 2-year age difference and that stops me from fitting in.

I see everyone with all their friends and see them smile and laugh and they are having a good time.

While I am just sitting by myself I think, why am I different to you all? Everyone is different in their own way.

I guess that's how the world sees people these days. But I know that I am loved by God and that he created me special. In the end that is what really matters.

By Maddy

Here are some things you can try if you
are feeling this way:

Make a list of all the people in your life
who matter to you.

Write a children's book
and illustrate it.

Make cards to sell so you can
raise money for a charity.

Pray and ask God to help you see how
truly amazing and worthwhile you are.

Clean out your wardrobe and donate clothes
and shoes that don't fit any more to charity.

Take photographs of
your 50 favourite things.

Make Christmas cards
(even if it's April!).

Design and create a veggie patch (you will need to ask Mum and Dad's permission first). Just think how much fun it will be to eat your own vegetables. ☺

Spend some time doing something you enjoy e.g. singing, dancing to your favourite music, reading, shopping, cooking.

Have a movie marathon – watch all your favourite movies in one afternoon/evening.

Write a card or a letter to someone important in your life (maybe a friend or relative who lives far away).

Often when we DO something for SOMEONE ELSE – even when we don't really feel like it AT ALL – we can feel much better afterwards. Cool, eh?

Ideas from...

♥ REAL GIRLS

'Plan with a group of friends to write
special notes to each other, telling them
about all the things you love about them. Each person
gets a name and they write an anonymous letter.'

Shauna

'Mums and dads can sometimes annoy us, but they also
know about lots of things, including friends. Spend some time
chatting with your mum or dad or a grown-up you can trust,
and you'll realise that they can be a great support/help.
And remember, nothing is forever. Things will get better!
And if they aren't looking like they are, have a chat to your
mum or dad and see what can be done to help (i.e. moving
classes or schools).'

Jazz

'Do something for somebody else, e.g. help your mum with
the dishes or clean up your brother's or sister's toys.
Helping other people makes you feel more positive. Making a
difference in someone else's life helps shift the focus away
from you and your own problems.'

Talitha

'I try to look at the things I'm good
at and what I've achieved in life already.
The things that have made me feel or
be important. Or I reach out to another
person who may often be the one who gets
left out. Instead of feeling sorry for myself and thinking about
me, I try to turn it around and get to know someone new.
As I'm doing it, I forget that I was feeling down.

'Not that I do this next one very often but maybe I should
do it more — that is, to look at the promises God has made
about how he feels about me. That's a lot clearer than the
foggy feeling I have about myself and is all true.'

Katie

'Try and get involved with multiple groups of people so your
whole life isn't just school friends. By doing other activities
and mixing with new people and a variety of people, it
improves your self-confidence. So cast your net wide to
get a variety of friends, then spend the most time with the
friends who make you feel good about yourself.'

Lisa

'Sometimes, when I feel down in the dumps, I sit down with my sister or my mum and we watch some of my DVDs, just to be close to one another and know that in the end, we're not truly alone. Sometimes, I sit and watch my dad in his workshop, and listen to him give endless talks on the tools and what he's doing, despite the fact I have little idea what he's talking about. But it gives me joy to see him so happy and passionate there. Or I spend time with my dogs, taking them for a walk or playing with them. I'm lucky enough to have two puppies. Sometimes, when I get home from a terrible day at school, and I really don't want to do anything but moan, the animals get so excited to see you when you get home after long hours! They love you unconditionally if you treat them right, and they can always put a smile on your face.'

Katherine

'Friends are amazing. But they come and go, and you never know how long you'll have them. You can't depend on others to always hold the key to your joy. Life doesn't work like that. Unless they are offering ice cream — THEN, they hold a key to happiness.'

Sarah

'Invite some friends over. If friends
are the problem, then have a good cry;
then talk with your mum.'

Sienna

'Channel your put-out feelings into something that gives
YOU joy. Paint, write, stand in front of the mirror with a
hairbrush (or a shampoo bottle) and pretend you're on
stage performing. Perhaps you like baking? Get together
with your mum or older sibling and make some cupcakes
and share them with your family.'

Caitlin

'Spend some time in prayer. I often find if I'm feeling
a bit sad or unsure of myself I talk to God.
I just tell him how I'm feeling and it feels good
to know he listens and understands..'

Taylah

I moved to another part of the country and changed schools in Year 4 and knew absolutely no one at my new school.

Because I am naturally quite shy, it can be hard for others to get to know the real me.

For months, I would sit quietly in the classroom each day and only talk to other girls if they asked me a question or if the teacher asked us to work in pairs or small groups.

One day, our music teacher announced that she was starting a school choir and she would be holding auditions at lunchtime the next day.

Inside, I was a little bit **EXCITED** and **NERVOUS** – both at the same time. My mum encouraged me to step out of my comfort zone and go to the audition the next day.

I was worried about what the other girls might say or think of my voice, but I knew deep down that I really loved to sing.

After the auditions, my music teacher told me that I had a lovely singing voice and a real gift! This made me feel so happy and excited.

Also, some of the girls from my class came up to me and told me I sang well. Their kind words and encouragement made me feel like I was important and that I had a gift to share.

After that day, I felt a **LOT MORE CONFIDENT** about getting to know some of the other girls in my class (and some of the other girls who also came to choir practice). I have now given others the chance to get to know me and I have also had the chance to make lots of new friends who mean a lot to me.

'You are an amazing girl
created in God's own image.
You don't have to
be anyone other than
WHO YOU ARE!
You are beautiful, unique
and treasured.
There has never been
another YOU...
and there never will be!'

Sharon Witt

The 21-day challenge to LOVING yourself more

'Be kind to everyone, including yourself.'

Unknown

I have heard of many versions of this type of challenge, however I really **LOVE** this from the creator of REAL GIRLS, Sam Corfield. (Thanks Sam for sharing this with us!) I have adapted these ideas from 'Real Girls'.

It has been said that in order to form a habit, it takes approximately **21 DAYS**. For example, if you are in the habit of biting your finger nails, once you begin to use different strategies to stop yourself, such as putting adhesive strips over each of your finger nails (GROSS!) or painting your nails with foul-tasting ointment (YUCK!), it will take approximately 21 days of consistent commitment. That means making sure you stick to it every day — so you can hopefully break the habit.

It can be challenging, but that's the point.
If it was **EASY**, it wouldn't be a challenge!

So the following challenge is a bit of a self-esteem
builder. If you are struggling with not feeling too great
about yourself, then this activity is for **YOU!**

It's about changing your THINKING and not FOCUSING
on the stuff you don't like about yourself. Instead, it
helps you focus on all that is AMAZING, **FANTASTIC** and
LOVABLE about YOU. So go ahead!

Give the following 21-day challenge a GO.

1 Create a list of FIVE THINGS you like about yourself and share it with at least one person.

2 Write down all the QUALITIES that make you a good person.

3 Read your BIBLE each day to hear what God thinks about you.

4 Write down where you see yourself in five years' time — this is an opportunity to really think about what it is you most DREAM of becoming.

5 What do you want to be REMEMBERED FOR? When you're 100 years-old, and you look back on your life and all you have accomplished, what do you want people to remember about you the most?

6 Find a QUOTE that most sums you up and put it somewhere where you will see it every day.

Adapted from the '21-day challenge' by Samantha Corfield.

7 Ask three people to write a list of things they LOVE ABOUT YOU and keep it to read.

8 Make a list of ALL the things you are GRATEFUL for in your life.

9 Write a list of all the negative things you tell yourself and then rip it up and throw it away.

10 Create a playlist of SONGS that make you feel good about yourself.

11 Treat yourself to a 'PICK-ME-UP' — read a book, take a bath, listen to music — anything that will allow you to relax and take a moment for you.

12 Do something BY YOURSELF. Watch a movie, tend your garden bed, paint a picture. You will be surprised at how empowering it can be.

13 What are you most PROUD of about yourself? Write it down and share it.

14 Give back to others. It is amazing how GIVING TO OTHERS can really make us feel better about ourselves and put life into a completely new perspective.

15 Think about a part of your body you don't like and write down something that you DO like about it.

16 Try something NEW. If there is something you have always wanted to do but never have done — get out there and DO IT! You never know — you may be better at it than you thought.

17 Take a PHOTO of a special place that is important to you.

18 Write a LOVE LETTER to yourself explaining how beautiful and amazing you are!

19 Think about your BEST FRIEND. What are three qualities you really love about that person? Let the person know and put an unexpected smile on her face!

20 Create a list of people you ADMIRE and why. This is important as it says a lot about the kind of person you are. I've heard it said, 'You can only admire in others what your heart calls its own truth'. Stand in that truth and be what you admire!

21 Now that you've made it to Day 21, write a list of ALL the things you LOVE about yourself. See if you can see a change in yourself between the way you were feeling on Day 1 and now.

A true friend

Friends stick by you
When you are down
And give you a smile
Instead of a frown.

A true friend is caring
And compliments you;
Helps you through things
Whatever you do.

A friend encourages you
When you feel good
And supports you
As every friend should.

To have a true friend
That is good,
You have to be one back,
Like they would.

Anonymous

MORE ABOUT YOU

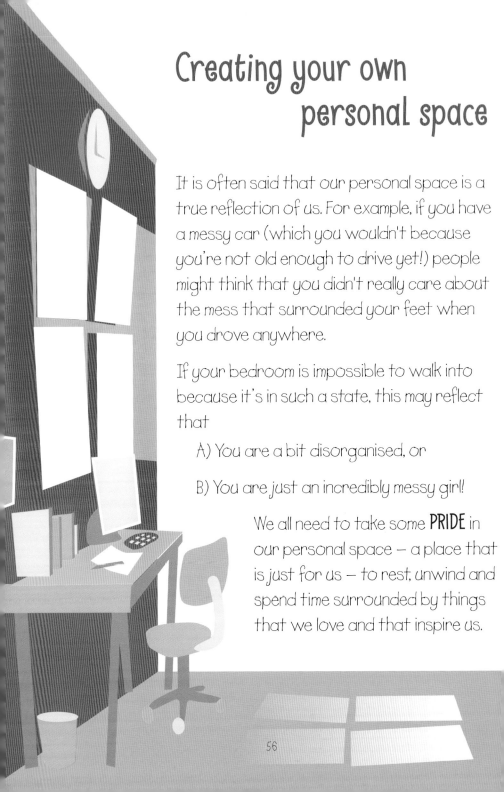

Creating your own personal space

It is often said that our personal space is a true reflection of us. For example, if you have a messy car (which you wouldn't because you're not old enough to drive yet!) people might think that you didn't really care about the mess that surrounded your feet when you drove anywhere.

If your bedroom is impossible to walk into because it's in such a state, this may reflect that

A) You are a bit disorganised, or

B) You are just an incredibly messy girl!

We all need to take some **PRIDE** in our personal space – a place that is just for us – to rest, unwind and spend time surrounded by things that we love and that inspire us.

You may be lucky enough to have your own bedroom at home, or at least a space in a shared bedroom that is just for you.

I have a small office at the front of my home where I write. Above my desk, I have a collection of photos of important people in my life and people who inspire me – role models.

I also have photos of special times, places I have visited and most importantly, quotes and Bible verses that I love and which always encourage me and lift my spirits when I am working. I also surround myself with many books, candles and pretty wall signs.

I love pinks, whites, blues and greens in pastel shades so I always have stationery and accessories that reflect peace and calm. Also, they look very pretty!

What does your personal space say about you?

If you are anything like I was as a young lady, your bedroom may be very cluttered and messy. When I was growing up, you could barely walk on the carpet, and I threw all of my clothes and shoes onto my floordrobe.

I often felt anxious and unsettled when I was in my room because it was so messy and totally disorganised. It was so messy that it even attracted a mouse once, making me run away!

If you are lucky enough to have your own room, or special space in your room, take some time to make it a space that reflects who you are. Make it **SPECIAL** in a way that inspires you.

For example, you could write out or type on a computer a few of your favourite quotes or Bible verses – we've included some on the following pages for you as inspiration. Put these quotes into an inexpensive photo frame to display on your wall. Why not purchase a few frames and make a wall display!

Inspiring quotes and verses

'For beautiful eyes,
look for the good in others,
for beautiful lips,
speak only words of kindness,
and for poise,
walk with the knowledge
that you are never alone.'

Audrey Hepburn

'Don't let comparison steal your joy.'

Unknown

'You are the light of the world. A town built on a hill cannot be hidden. Neither do people light a lamp and put it under a bowl. Instead they put it on its stand, and it gives light to everyone in the house. In the same way, let your light shine before others, that they may see your good deeds and glorify your Father in heaven.'

Matthew 5:14 (NIV)

'Be kind to everyone including yourself.'

Anonymous

'It takes courage to grow up and become who you really are.'

E.E. Cummings

'If God brings you to it, he will bring you through it.'

Anonymous

'You are God's created beauty and the focus of His affection and delight.'

Janet L. Smith

'We all have ability. The difference is how we use it.'

Stevie Wonder

'You are the only person on earth who can use your ability.'

Zig Ziglar

'We don't know who we are until we can see what we can do.'

Martha Grimes

Your own personal space

Use the space below to make a dream list of all the things you would like to surround yourself with in your personal space.

Inspiration board

You will need:

* A medium or large pinboard (available from department stores, discount stores and stationery outlets)

* Cotton material to cover board (optional)

* Craft glue

* Photos of friends and family

* Pictures of role models and things that inspire you.

* Favourite quotes and Bible verses

* Scrapbooking supplies (if you have them)

Some pinboards already come in funky colours, but you can easily make a personal inspiration board by covering the front in some bright or inspiring fabric and gluing it on the back of the board with craft glue.

Once dry, you can make a border using some scrapbooking paper or matching fabric.

Then you can set about filling your **INSPIRATION BOARD** with pictures, photos, quotes, Bible verses, dreams, places you'd like to visit, things you want to achieve – or anything else you can think of.

It is YOUR inspiration board and it is a reflection of YOU and all your memories, dreams and future dreams.

An attitude of gratitude

'Gratitude turns what we have into enough.'

Unknown

Some days, we can all feel a little, well, **Bleeeerrrggghhh!**

I sometimes have days when I wake up and everything seems to be DREARY and GREY. Even adults have yucky bleerrgh days! And when you have one of those days, it is just so easy to see the things that are not right in our world or things that we're not doing so well at.

For example, if you are having a yucky day, you can find yourself FOCUSING on all the homework you have to complete for school, how messy your bedroom is and how Mum and Dad keep asking you to do chores around the house while not fighting with your brother!

It's just so easy to focus on the **NEGATIVE** and yucky feelings or things we're not doing so well at.

One of the best things I have learnt to do is try and find one thing that I can be grateful for each day – even, and ESPECIALLY on those BLEERRGHH days.

For example, you could be grateful for:

A bed to sleep in at night

The blessing of being able to go to school

Your faith

Good friends

Your talents

Your mum and dad

A warm shower

Music

Gratitude in a jar!

'Rejoice today and be glad.'

Psalm 118:24b (NIV)

Get a largish glass jar. It can be a large jam jar, for example. Make sure it's clean. You can also purchase glass jars with lids from a supermarket or discount store very cheaply.

You can decorate your special jar with paper, sequins, stickers, rhinestones, ribbons and lettering.

You might like to label it 'MY GRATITUDE JAR'.

Collect some coloured paper and cut it into small note-size pieces.

Now, each day for the next 30 days, take a moment daily to write down **ONE THING** you are grateful for.

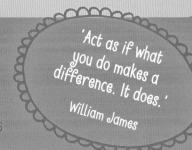

'Act as if what you do makes a difference. It does.'

William James

It might be that you are grateful for a warm room to sleep in each night, or that you are one of the fortunate girls that have the privilege of going to school to receive an education (when millions of children in third world countries do not have this opportunity).

It might be that you have nice clothes or can play an instrument. Whatever it is, **WRITE DOWN ONE THING EACH DAY** that you can be grateful or **THANKFUL** for.

At the end of the 30 days, spend some time laying all of the gratitude notes on your floor or bed and read all the **AMAZING** things you have to be thankful for in your life.

'People often forget that kindness is free.'

Unknown

'Gratitude turns what we have into enough.'

Melody Beattie

YOU are a part of…

We were never expected to go through life on our own and figure everything out by ourselves.

That's why we have been blessed by being part of a community. This means we **ALWAYS** have people in our immediate and wider circles who we can turn to for help, guidance and influence.

Firstly, you are part of a **FAMILY.** That is pretty awesome because being part of a family means you always belong. No one can take that away from you!

There are many different types of families. You might live with your mum and dad and siblings (brothers and sisters) or just one parent. Or you may even live with an aunt, uncle or grandparents, or even foster parents. In any case, YOU belong to a family.

Sometimes, situations might be tough within your family, and you might feel like you are an outsider, not fitting in.

But always remember that YOU MATTER!

YOU are **LOVED!**

YOU belong!

YOU are cared about!

YOU are part of something special!

YOU are part of a **FAMILY!**

And your family would never be the same without **YOU** in it!

You might also be a PART of...

* A choir
* Your class at school
* Your church
* A netball or basketball team
* A dance troupe
* A sports team
* Extended family
* A craft group
* A writing group
* A gymnastics team
* A horse riding club
* A football team

Make a list here of all the groups that **YOU** are a part of:

* ....
* ....
* ....
* ....
* crahth
  ....
* ....
* ....
* ....
* ....
* ....

Who do you look up to?

When I was younger, there were a few people I looked up to and really admired.

One of them was my favourite teacher, Mrs O'Neill.

I had her for two whole years and she was very FRIENDLY, **ENCOURAGING** and FAIR.

One day, while playing a ball game at breaktime, I got really frustrated and threw a stone at a boy when he got me out (I know, not very kind!) I was so shocked at what I had done that I did what most kids my age might have done.

I ran!

Once I calmed down, I knew I had to face my teacher and admit to what I had done wrong and face the consequences (punishment).

Mrs O'Neill was very fair and patient with me and helped me learn the best way to apologise to the boy I had hurt and how to move on.

I also looked up to another adult – my Sunday school teacher at church. She was always encouraging and I always looked forward to spending time with her on Sunday mornings. She would think up creative ways of teaching us stories and lessons from the Bible.

I also greatly admired my mum, and still do.

She worked very hard, both inside our home – washing my clothes, making me yummy dinners, and more – but also worked as a nurse, caring for young children who were severely disabled and needed extra care outside their homes.

I looked up to many celebrities and singers, including Kylie Minogue, who I thought was amazingly talented.

I even wrote to Kylie at the television studio where she worked. Imagine my great surprise and excitement when I actually received a handwritten reply, along with a photograph.

I had asked Kylie a couple of questions about how she came to be a television actress and she actually wrote back with some helpful advice!

ROLE MODELS are often people you admire and may seek advice from or spend time with. But the great thing is that you don't have to personally know someone for that person to be a role model.

For example, you might admire a sports person, actor, singer, band member, politician or even an astronaut!

Many famous or well-known people have their own websites or fan sites that allow you to find out some more information about them or ask questions. Some people may have even written a book about their success or journey that you could borrow from the library. You may even like to write a letter to someone you admire. You just never know – you might be lucky like I was and receive a reply.

But your **ROLE MODEL** can be someone as wonderful as your big sister, aunt, mum or even your teacher. They don't have to be famous or even that incredible.

Your own role models

Make a list here of your **OWN** role models
and what you admire about them.

Remember: you don't need to have personally met them.

You can make a difference!

'What you do makes a difference,
and you have to decide what kind of difference
you want to make.'

Jane Goodall

You may think that because you're not yet grown up you cannot make a difference in this world. Well listen up! I'm here to tell you that you absolutely, positively **CAN!**

Firstly, you can begin by MAKING A DIFFERENCE in your immediate surroundings, such as within your family, class at school or friendship group.

You could start by helping mum and dad prepare dinner one night a week — make sure you check with them first. Or put the bins out without asking. Maybe clear away the dinner dishes each night. Or perhaps you might be kind enough to sit down and help your little brother with his homework project at night, or listen to him practise his reading.

Perhaps you notice someone at school who never gets invited to be part of a group or is never chosen to be part of a team during sport. By making a conscious decision to go out of your way to ask someone to join in and be included, you might just make that person's day.

YOU CAN NEVER UNDERESTIMATE THE DIFFERENCE THAT SMALL GESTURES CAN MAKE!

'When we give cheerfully and accept gratefully, everyone is blessed.'

Mayo Angelou

The starfish story

I have heard this story many times and I never get sick of hearing it. It's a great little story about making a difference no matter how small...

A man was wandering along a beach at dusk when he noticed an incredible sight before him. Hundreds and hundreds of starfish had washed up onto the sand. Without being in the safety of the ocean, they would surely die.

The man observed a boy in the distance picking up and throwing something into the ocean. On closer inspection, the man soon realised that the young boy was bending down, picking up a starfish and tossing it back into the safety of the ocean.

The man approached the boy and spoke to him about what he saw as a totally pointless task.

'Hey buddy,' he said. 'Don't you realise that there are hundreds and hundreds of starfish stranded on this beach. You cannot possibly make a difference.
The task is impossible!'

The young boy picked up another starfish, tossing it back into the ocean.

'Made a difference to THAT one!' he replied.

So you see, you CAN make a difference by being faithful even in the smallest ways.

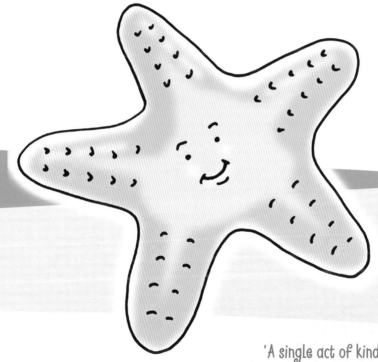

'A single act of kindness
throws out roots in all directions,
and the roots spring up
and make new trees.'

Amelia Earhart

Girls just like YOU
making a DIFFERENCE!

Mikaela

Mikaela was just 10 years old when she decided that she wanted to make a difference to people suffering from cancer. She chose to shave off all of her long, brown hair to raise money for cancer research.

She signed up for 'World's Greatest Shave' and set about raising donations from family, friends and teachers before having all of her hair shaved off by a teacher, right in front of her entire junior school assembly.

Through that effort, she was able to raise more than a thousand pounds for cancer research. It was an amazing thing for a young girl to do - especially as she had to go through several months without hair, having to wear hats to keep her head warm in winter!

Jem and Em

Jemma and Emily were 11 years old when they decided to put their creativity and love of crafts to good use. They combined their creative talents to raise money, making greeting cards to support an orphanage in a developing country.

The girls set up a website, took photos and advertised their personalised greeting cards and even created order forms. Jemily & Co was off and running.
Very soon, they began selling their beautiful handmade cards to family, friends and teachers at school.
And whilst they were helping children they may never meet, they were having fun too.

Anna

Anna was 11 years old when she had the opportunity to travel with a group from her church to India. While there, she visited an orphanage. In the orphanage Anna played with children, sang songs and played games to bring some joy to the lives of those she met.

The wonderful thing about this experience was that it helped spread some love and joy to the children she met, but it also changed Anna's heart. Now she wants to continue making a difference to orphanages such as the one she visited.

'What we do is less than
a drop in the ocean.
But if that drop were
missing,
the ocean would lack
something.'

Mother Teresa

What could YOU do?

Just imagine for a moment how **YOU** could make a difference in the lives of others? It may be doing something for people you know, or others you have never met.

Write some ideas below. DARE TO DREAM!

Girls who change the world

There are girls who make things better...

simply by showing up.

There are girls who make things happen,

Girls who make their way.

There are girls who make a difference,

Girls who make us smile.

There are girls who do not make excuses,

girls who cannot be replaced.

There are girls of wit and wisdom who —

with strength and courage — make it through.

There are girls who change the world
        every day...

Girls like YOU.

Ashley Rice

What do you want to do when you GROW UP?

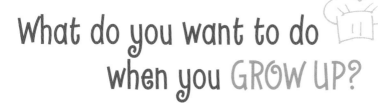

Have you ever sat and thought about what you might like to do or be when you GROW UP?

Perhaps you **LOVE** to play with animals and care for them. Or you might really enjoy helping out at crèche or Sunday school at church. You may even dream of becoming the next Prime Minister! We all have the same opportunity to become whatever it is we want to become and do what we dream to do.

When I was younger, I wanted to be an actress on television. Then I was interested in nursing. I did end up working in television for a while, but my real passion was working with young people – and so I became a teacher. It wasn't until I was much older that I discovered that I really LOVED to write.

You never have to truly decide what you want to be because you may change careers many times, or you might study to become a vet and then decide you would much rather work with children than animals.

Make sure you try and find something that you ENJOY!

What do you want to be when you GROW UP?

'An author or an art teacher and a fashion designer, because I love writing stories and I love to draw dresses on people.'

Erica, aged 12

'I want to be a horse trainer when I grow up because I love working with animals. My favourite animal is a horse.'

Alex, aged 12

'I would love to be a nurse because I love to help people and I want everyone to be healthy.'

Savannah, aged 12

'When I grow up, I want to be a professional basketballer.'

Georgia, aged 12

'In Year 4, all I wanted to be was a teacher.
My friends and I were so obsessed that we used
to pretend to teach our teddy bears. We even held
"Staff Meetings" at the kitchen table!'

Renee, aged 11

'I want to be a teacher and a child-care worker.'

Sophie, aged 9

'I have always wanted to be a rock star.
I love to sing!'

Jess, aged 10

'I'd like to be a doctor so I could help
other people who are sick.'

Joyce, aged 10

'I want to be either a doctor, artist, author/
illustrator or an art teacher. I can't decide!'

Lia, aged 10

'I want to be a pop star when I grow up.
If I can't be a pop star I want to be a doctor.'

Andrea, aged 10

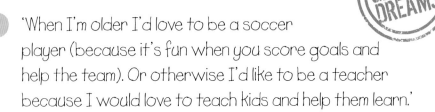

'When I'm older I'd love to be a soccer player (because it's fun when you score goals and help the team). Or otherwise I'd like to be a teacher because I would love to teach kids and help them learn.'

Dakota, aged 9

'I want to work at an aquarium when I grow up because I love dolphins, fish, turtles, sharks and other sea creatures.'

Stephanie, aged 10

'When I grow up I want to be a fashion designer and own a fashion store.'

Sienna, aged 10

'When I grow up I want to run a training school for puppies because I just adore puppies.'

Yasmine, aged 11

'I want to be a pastry chef when I grow up. I just love to cook, and taste great food.'

Shula, aged 10

JUST
FOR FUN

Choc chip cookies

 Time allowance: 1 hour, plus clean-up time

What you'll need

- ✔ Large mixing bowl
- ✔ Tea spoon
- ✔ Wooden spoon
- ✔ Fork
- ✔ Baking trays x2
- ✔ Kitchen scales
- ✔ Greaseproof paper (so your cookies don't stick to the tray)
- ✔ A seive for the flour

Ingredients (what you'll need to make these yummy bikkies)

- ✔ 175g cups self-raising flour
- ✔ 150 g butter
- ✔ 125g of white sugar
- ✔ 1 egg
- ✔ Vanilla essence
- ✔ 1 small bag of chocolate chips – these are found in the baking aisle of the supermarket

Method (how you actually make them)

1 First, make sure an adult is with you because you will need to do some cooking. Also, wash your hands first.

2 Turn the oven on to 180 degrees Celsius or gas mark 4. You will need to ask for your mum or dad's help here!

3 Allow the butter to soften out of the fridge.

4 In a bowl, mix together the butter and sugar.

5 Once they are mixed through, add in your egg and mix together.

6 Add a little swish of vanilla essence (maybe a teaspoonful). This will give your cookies some extra yummy flavour. ☺

7 Sift in the self-raising flour. Mix all the ingredients together well so that no flour is left unmixed.

8 Finally, stir in the entire bag of yummy chocolate chips. If you want to make something different, you can use M&M's or Smarties. Just be careful to mix them in gently so that the colour doesn't run all through your mixture.

9 Cut greaseproof paper to fit on the base of your trays.

10 Using a teaspoon dipped in water, spoon small balls of mixture onto the baking trays (about 12 on each tray).

11 Make sure they have enough room to spread out because they WILL get wider when they cook.

12 Using a fork dipped in warm water, flatten each ball of dough out, and you are **READY** to pop these yummy cookies in the oven. ☺

13 Bake for about 15 minutes, or until they look light brown.

Take them out of the oven and allow to cool.

Enjoy with your family ☺

YUMMY!

Snuggle buggle blanket

Who doesn't **LOVE** to just snuggle up
on the couch on a cold, rainy day and
watch a favourite movie or read a book?

This snuggle buggle blanket doesn't require ANY
sewing, however you will need to ask your mum or
another adult to take you to the material store to buy
the correct material, and supervise.

 Time allowance: 1-3 hours

What you'll need:

- ✔ 1 pair of scissors (sharp enough to cut material).
- ✔ Polar fleece material — choose your favourite pattern at the store. You will need a square cut — about 1.5 metres by 1.5 metres.
- ✔ A second piece of polar fleece exactly the same size, in a plain colour. (Make sure the plain colour matches your patterned piece.)
- ✔ Dressmaking pins to pin the material together.

Method (how you'll make your gorgeous blanket)

1. Find a clear space on the floor where you can lay your material out FLAT.

2. You will need to lay the plain piece first (with the wrong side facing upwards). The GOOD side of your material needs to face the floor.

3. Get your second piece of polar fleece and lay it carefully and evenly on top of the other piece. (This is where *mum* would be handy to help you get it flat and straight!) The GOOD (or patterned) side needs to face YOU this time (good side up).

4. Make sure all four corners of both pieces of fabric meet up. You don't want a wonky blanket.

5. Using the pins, connect each corner gently together, but be very CAREFUL not to pin yourself – OUCH!

6. Using your scissors, cut four corners out of the material – make sure you get through both pieces of fabric.

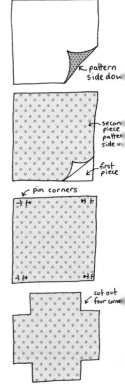

pattern side dow

secon piece patter side u

first piece

pin corners

cut out four corne

7 Starting on one side, begin to cut a straight line about 8cm long into the material. Leaving gaps, cut lines through all the way along until you get to the next corner.

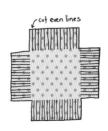
cut even lines

It will take a while because you need to be careful to keep the cuts EVEN and not **TOO CLOSE TOGETHER.**

8 Once you have cut through one whole edge, you are now ready to make the TASSELS and begin joining your two pieces of fabric together.

Tie each double piece of fabric together in a double knot – at the base of the cut (see diagram). NOTE: Don't pull the knots too tight or the material may rip apart.

tie here

repeat tie all the way around

9 Do the same with each side of your blanket until all the tassels of your new blanket are done.

Enjoy snuggling with your blanket ☺

These are a **GREAT** idea to make for a birthday present or GIFT for a friend.

Paper bag albums

 Time allowance: 1-3 hours

What you will need:

- ✔ 2-3 large paper bags
- ✔ Glue stick
- ✔ Craft scissors
- ✔ Photographs of friends and family
- ✔ Scrapbooking paper
- ✔ Favourite quotes/images

Let's get started!

1 Place two or three paper bags together and fold together sideways so that they look like a booklet. You can ask mum to use her sewing machine – if she has one – to sew a line straight down the centre (like a book). Or you can use ribbon or staples to hold the centre together.

Once your album pages have been joined together, you can begin the exciting task of creating the pages of your journal/album.

2 Trim bag edges so that all the pages open out.

3 Trace the outline of your album onto the scrapbooking paper using a grey lead pencil. Cut out. Using your glue stick, paste the paper onto your individual pages.

4 Make sure you cover the front and back covers as well.

5 Now you are ready to add your favourite quotes, photographs and memories.

Time capsule — a great activity to do with a friend

This is a fun activity to do with a friend one weekend or during a sleepover.

The idea of a time capsule is that you write yourself a letter to read some time in the future, or for someone else to read. You include in your capsule some reminders of the year you are currently living in and some of the things you love and are popular at this time.

You can choose to fill your container with as many things as will fit, however you should also write a note that explains what each of the items are and why you included them.

Make sure you keep a record somewhere of where you actually bury your time capsule! When I was in primary school, our entire school contributed to a time capsule that would be opened 30 years later... except... no one could remember where it was buried! (Whoops!)

What you'll need:

- ✔ A metal or plastic container (needs to be watertight).
- ✔ Approximately 10 plastic sleeves/protectors.
- ✔ Coloured card and pens.
- ✔ Sticky tape.
- ✔ Large plastic bag.
- ✔ Writing paper to record why you have chosen to include each item.

Things you could include:

- ✔ A collection of some of your favourite photographs (see if you can get copies so you don't lose them forever). Pop them in a few plastic sheet protectors.
- ✔ A few current coins.
- ✔ The front page of a recent newspaper.
- ✔ A postage stamp.
- ✔ A plastic bag, large enough to hold your plastic or tin container.
- ✔ Pictures cut from a magazine of your favourite celebrities, actors and bands or singers.
- ✔ A letter to your 'future self', telling yourself where you would like to be in the future, what you'd like to do when you leave school, where you'd like to travel, and more.

✔ A few examples of your school work.

✔ Your favourite Bible verses.

Method (how to make the time capsule)

1. Make sure you find a place in your garden where you are allowed to dig a hole. It's a good idea to ask Mum or Dad first.

2. Once you have filled your time capsule with all your special memories and keepsakes, seal the lid with a layer of sticky tape (just to make sure it is sealed) before wrapping in a plastic bag.

3. You need to bury your time capsule a fair way down (at least half a metre). You might like to erect a sign or place a special plant to remind you where it is buried. But most importantly, write the location down — somewhere you won't forget.

4. Decide how many years you will wait until you dig up your capsule. Maybe the last day of secondary school or when you move out of home.

All time favourite GIRLS' movies
– voted for by girls

Why not plan a girls' night in, get some popcorn and snuggle up and watch a cool girls' movie. ☺

* Ella Enchanted
* Matilda
* Annie
* The Wizard of OZ
* Mrs Doubtfire
* Hotel for Dogs
* Cat in the Hat
* Soul Surfer (check with parents first!)
* Finding Nemo
* The Secret Garden
* Monte Carlo
* Nancy Drew
* Disney movies
* Enchanted

Favourite books to read

As voted by girls JUST like YOU!

❋ Diary of a Wimpy Kid series – Jeff Kinney

❋ Tales of a 4th Grade Nothing – Judy Blume

❋ Charlie and the Chocolate Factory – Roald Dahl

❋ The Kingdom is Silk — Glenda Millard

❋ Swallows and Amazons series – Arthur Ransome

❋ Deltora Quest series – Emily Rodda

❋ Little House on the Prairie series
   – Laura Ingalls Wilder

❋ Anne of Green Gables series – L.M. Montgomery

❋ Nancy Drew series – Carolyn Keene

❋ The Famous Five series – Enid Blyton

❋ The Secret Seven series – Enid Blyton

❋ Charlotte's Web – E.B. White

❋ A Wrinkle in Time – Madeleine L'Engle

* The Chronicles of Narnia - C.S. Lewis

* Best Friends – Jacqueline Wilson

* The Secret Garden – F.H. Burnett

* The Borrowers – Mary Norton

* Judy Moody series – Megan McDonald

* The Sheep-Pig – Dick King-Smith

* The Keepers series – Lian Tanner

* Thea Stilton series – Thea Stilton

* Heidi – Johanna Spyri

* Picnic at Hanging Rock – Joan Lindsay

* The Wind in the Willows – Kenneth Grahame

* Watership Down – Richard Adams

* Tarka the Otter – Henry Williamson

TODAY

Choose today to be the very best version of **YOU.**

Choose today to **LOVE** the person that you are.

Choose today to look for the best in others.

Choose today to dream new dreams.

Choose today to forgive someone who upsets you.

Choose today to make wise choices.

Choose today to make a difference.

Choose today to be AMAZING.

Choose today to be a positive influence on others.

Choose today to do something nice for someone else.

Choose today to encourage.

Choose today to SHINE!

'For I know the plans I have for you,' declares the LORD, 'plans to prosper you and to not harm you, plans to give hope and a future.'

Jeremiah 29:11 (NIV)

FEELINGS

Feelings

Your feelings are an important part of what makes you, YOU.

Each and every day, you will experience many different FEELINGS and EMOTIONS.

You might feel excited, shy, sad, angry, scared, **HAPPY**, stressed, tired, energetic or embarrassed.

Sometimes, you might experience several FEELINGS all at the same time.

Your teacher might announce that your class will be going on a school trip this term, which will mean two nights spent away from home.

You might feel **EXCITED, HAPPY** and NERVOUS and SCARED all mixed in.

It is perfectly normal to feel many feelings at once.

It just means that you are capable of feeling a variety emotions, which is just the way YOU WERE CREATED.

If your feelings start to bother you — especially if you are feeling **NERVOUS**, SCARED, **FRIGHTENED, ANGRY** or

SAD – it is a good idea to share these feelings with another person, especially an **ADULT** in your life.

You might talk to your mum, dad, teacher, aunty or uncle or grandparents. It is important that you do talk to someone about your negative feelings. That's because there are often things you can do to help yourself feel better about a situation.

Feelings I sometimes have:

Writing about MY feelings...

Describe a time when you felt **SAD**.
What helped you feel better?

....

....

....

Describe a time when you felt **HAPPY**.
What was happening at the time?

....

....

....

Describe a time when you felt **ANGRY**.
What helped you get through it?

....

....

....

Describe a time when you felt NERVOUS.
What helped you calm down?

....

....

....

Describe a time when you felt LONELY.
What helped you get through this time?

....

....

....

Describe a time when you felt EXCITED.
Why were you so excited and what happened?

....

....

....

Why does it feel like a thousand BUTTERFLIES are in my stomach?

Sometimes it can feel like there are hundreds, if not thousands, of little butterflies all having a party in our stomachs. Have you ever felt that?

It might be just before you have to stand up in front of the class and read something out or give a small speech.

Or perhaps you have just had an argument with your parents or a friend and you know deep down that you have done or said the wrong thing.

This butterfly feeling in our stomach comes from our FEELINGS, just letting us know that they are there. It is not something to be frightened of – there aren't REALLY thousands of butterflies in your stomach!

Sometimes, these feelings are referred to as NERVES (from the word nervous). This is simply our body's way of letting us know that it is NERVOUS, WORRIED or perhaps a little AFRAID, or even just a bit EXCITED. This feeling in your stomach is nothing to worry about. It usually goes away once you have finishing making your speech, or apologised to your friend if you hurt their feelings or said sorry to your mum and dad.

Getting rid of the butterflies

* Take five strong, deep breaths

* Remember that you **CAN** do it!

* Pray! Ask God to help you get through it

* Take a walk to get some air

* Listen to some calming music

No one can make you feel UPSET or ANGRY

You always have a choice as to how you will react

Have you ever said, '**YOU** make me **SO** angry!' or '**YOU** made me get **UPSET**!'

I know that I've said that.

I think we **ALL** have at times. Importantly, though, no one can actually **MAKE** us feel upset, angry or hurt. We ourselves actually have full control of how we think, react and behave in most, if not all, circumstances.

Now when we are younger (like you gorgeous girl!) it can take some time to understand this and take control of our own thoughts and reactions. It does actually take some **PRACTICE**.

For example, I remember when I was a young girl, my brother used to tease me about the shape of my nose. He always made comments and pulled faces because he KNEW that I would react. Usually, I reacted to those comments in a very upset or angry manner! That is exactly the reaction he was after!

As I grew older — and a little wiser — I realised that actually, I ALWAYS had a CHOICE as to how I reacted. I could choose to get angry and upset and yell nasty words back at him, or I could choose to pretend his words didn't hurt me, or walk away. I was always in control of my reactions.

Now, I must admit, I am still not always very good at controlling my reactions to things. Sometimes, as an adult, I still can over-react and get UPSET at things people say or events that take place around me. But I try to remember that no one else can make me upset or angry — that is entirely up to me.

Make a DIARY

Have you ever written your thoughts, feelings and ideas down in a diary?

Some girls love to create their own diaries and have a private space JUST FOR THEM to record feelings, thoughts, ideas or problems. It's a great habit to get into, even if you don't think you're any good at writing. The thing is, nobody except YOU will read it! (So make sure you have a really cool hiding place. ☺)

Things you will need:

 A small exercise book, or notebook

 Scrapbooking paper or wrapping paper

 Stickers and quotes

 Rhinestones (imitation jewels) or other add-ons

 Glue stick

 Scissors

1. Put the exercise book, open, onto the wrapping paper or scrapbook paper and trace around it so that you make an outline of your exercise book. Cut out the shape about 2cm bigger than the outline all around, so that you have enough extra to be able to fold over the edges to glue down on the cover.

2. Place glue over the front and back of your exercise book and stick it to the paper.

3. Cut off the corners, then fold the extra paper over onto the inside of the exercise book's cover and glue down (see picture).

4. Once you have covered your book, you are now ready to decorate your diary with whatever stickers, jewels and quotes you would like. Make it personal so that it reflects YOU!

You are now free to use your very own diary however you like!

EXERCISE BOOK

TRACE

Today I made my diary!

FOLD AND GLUE

WRAPPING PAPER

Some ideas to get your diary happening:

- Favourite song titles
- What you are grateful for today
- How was your day?
- Thoughts and feelings
- Problems you are working through
- What stresses you out?
- Favourite quotes
- Favourite Bible verses
- Song ideas and lyrics
- 50 things you'd like to do before you become an adult
- 10 books you've LOVED
- Places you'd like to visit

It's okay to make mistakes

'Just because you fail once,
doesn't mean you're gonna fail at everything.
Keep trying, hold on
and always believe in yourself.'

Marilyn Monroe

We will **ALL** make mistakes or experience failure at some stage. In fact you will make many mistakes in your lifetime. Even as an adult!

This is not something to worry about when it does happen. It is a normal part of life and I have not met one person who has NEVER made a mistake or experienced failure.

Sometimes, your mistake might be as simple as forgetting to make your bed in the morning or return a library book at school. The point is, it's okay to make a mistake occasionally as long as you **LEARN** from your mistake.

Just imagine you are having a birthday party. You are allowed to invite 10 friends. You make a list of girls you spend time with but make a decision NOT to invite one person – even though you know it will hurt her feelings and cause her to feel left out. She may even be standing close by when you cheerfully hand around your birthday invitations.

After your birthday party, when everyone at school is discussing how much fun you all had, you may feel SAD and a little REGRETFUL (which means you wish you hadn't made the choice to not include the girl).

You cannot change the decision you made at the time but you CAN learn from the choices you make that don't turn out the way you wished. Next time you organise a party or a get-together, you will remember how you felt and hopefully make a different choice.

If you have a spelling test at school and do poorly at it, try not to WORRY. Don't look at it as a failure. Just remind yourself that you need to perhaps spend a little more time at home practising your spelling words before the next test.

Admit your mistakes. Say SORRY to someone if you've hurt that person, and move on. We all make mistakes!

Forgiveness

Sometimes in life, a friend, a family member or even your teacher might upset you, be a bit unkind or do the wrong thing by you.

This can be a really difficult thing to work through and your feelings might be hurt. If you are not careful, you might feel ANGRY and UPSET for a while and it may be worse each time you see that person.

It is really important that you FORGIVE the person who hurt you.

I know, I know, this is NOT always an easy thing to do! In fact, you may not even want to forgive the person and think they don't DESERVE to be forgiven. However, if you don't, this can cause you to feel ANXIOUS and UPSET (a bit like having a knot in your stomach!).

The person who hurt your feelings MAY offer you an apology and say sorry. But even if that person doesn't, you need to forgive anyway. Because it is YOU who needs to feel at peace.

You've done it!

But there's more to life after you finish this page...

I am **SO** happy that you have read through Girl Wise.

And I really hope and pray that you have gained some practical advice and help in how to handle some of the situations you may find yourself in.

Remember, you have many, many years of growing up ahead of you – both physically and emotionally.

Always remember that inside you is great wisdom, strength and courage, and that you will go far!

I believe in you and just know that you are going to make a **HUGE** difference in this world, because **YOU** are in it. ☺

Sharon Witt

...has been immersed in teen world for two decades in her role as a secondary teacher, mentor and presenter to teens and their parents around Australia.

She is a mother of two and regularly runs programmes for young people that provide support and help them realise their full potential.

She is also a regular media commentator on teen and parenting issues and is the author of the best-selling Teen Talk Series of books that have helped many thousands of young people navigate their adolescent journey.

Contact Sharon at:
sharon@sharonwitt.com.au

GCSE

Physics

HOMEWORK BOOK

Graham Booth

Letts

EDUCATIONAL

Every effort has been made to trace copyright holders and to obtain their permission for the use of copyright material. The author and publishers will gladly receive information enabling them to rectify any error or omission in subsequent editions.

First published 1997

Letts Educational
Aldine House
Aldine Place
London W12 8AW
Telephone: 0181 740 2266

Text: © Graham Booth 1997

Design and illustrations © BPP (Letts Educational) Ltd 1997

Design, page layout and illustrations: Ken Vail Graphic Design

British Library Cataloguing-in-Publication Data

A CIP record for this book is available from the British Library

ISBN 1 85758 570 4

Printed and bound in Great Britain by Ashford Colour Press, Gosport

Letts Educational is the trading name of BPP (Letts Educational) Ltd

CONTENTS

INTRODUCTION

Welcome to your homework book. Although this book on its own is a very useful source of homework, it has been specifically written to be used with Letts GCSE Physics classbook.

The numbers before the title of each of the homework units refer to the units of the GCSE Physics classbook. You will need to study all of the numbered units and some of the lettered units. Your teacher will give you guidance on which units to study.

The questions in this book have been divided into the same seven sections, labelled A to G, as in the Physics classbook:

A Electricity, electronics and magnetism

B Forces and motion

C Waves

D The Earth and its place in the Universe

E Energy

F Molecular physics

G Radioactivity

There is a bank of review questions for each of the seven sections. These are extra exam-style questions which can be used for revision and exam practice.

Each unit begins with a topic summary to remind you of the key points from the classbook, followed by a selection of questions, of varying style and difficulty. Most units have their questions divided by a line. Questions before the line are there to start you off on a topic. You should complete these before beginning the questions after the line.

To help you answer these questions when you are at home without your classbook, there is a reference section at the back of this book. This includes a glossary so that you can find out the meaning of any important scientific terms and a list of important formulae, physical quantities and their units.

It is becoming increasingly important to do regular homework if you want to do well. This homework book provides a valuable way to practise and reinforce what you do in class, and so help you to do your best and increase your enjoyment of Physics and Science.

A Electricity, electronics and magnetism

1–2 Current and energy transfer

- Current is not used up by electrical devices.
- Components connected in series must always have the same current.
- In a parallel circuit the current splits at a junction; the current passing into a junction must be the same as the current passing out.
- Currents consist of moving charges that transfer energy from the electricity supply into heat, light and movement when they pass through circuit components or domestic appliances.
- In metals the charge carriers are negatively charged electrons. Both positive and negative ions can move in ionised gases and electrolytes.

Q1 Write down the ammeter readings A1 to A3 in the circuit.

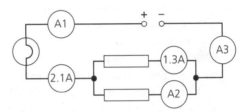

Q2 Which circuits allow either the lamp or motor, or both to be switched on?

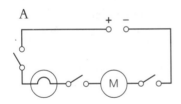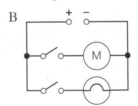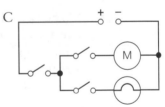

Q3 In normal operation, the current in a filament lamp is 0.25 A and that in a kettle element is 10.0 A. Which of the following statements is correct?
A The kettle uses more current than the lamp does.
B The lamp uses more current than the kettle does.
C More current is used in producing heat than in producing light.
D No current is used to produce heat or light.

Q4 Cars use low-voltage d.c. (direct current) circuits. The diagram shows some of the circuits in a car.
a) Which switches need to be on to light the headlamp?
b) Which switches need to be on to light the foglamp?
c) Draw a circuit diagram to show how the interior light in a car can be switched on by opening either the driver's door or the passenger door.

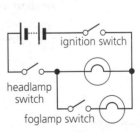

Q5 Draw diagrams to show the energy flow through:
a) a hairdryer
b) a kettle.

Q6 The table shows the energy transfer each second by some common domestic appliances.
a) Present this data in the form of a bar chart.
b) Put the appliances into three groups: those used for heating; for lighting; and for movement.

Appliance	Energy transfer each second/J
iron	1100
vacuum cleaner	800
microwave cooker	1300
fluorescent light	18
immersion heater	2500

c) What conclusion can you make about the relative amounts of energy transferred by each group of appliances?

Q7 The diagram represents some of the ions in a tube of neon gas that is conducting electricity.

a) Describe, and explain, the movement of both the positively charged and the negatively charged ions.
b) Suggest how further ionisation could be caused when these ions collide with neon atoms in the tube.

Q8 a) When a lamp is switched on a circuit is completed. Explain why charged particles travel slowly in the thick connecting wires and much more quickly in the thin filament.
b) Explain why the filament becomes hot but the connecting wires stay cool.

3 Current and its control

■ Components in parallel must all have the same voltage across them.
■ The sum of the voltages across the components in a series circuit is equal to the supply voltage.
■ The size of the current in a circuit or component depends on the resistance as well as the voltage.
■ Increasing the resistance in a circuit decreases the current. Increasing the voltage increases the current.

Q1 a) Write down the readings on the voltmeters V1 to V3.

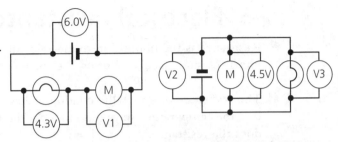

Q2 The table shows the current in a filament lamp and in a piece of nichrome wire (used in heating elements) for a range of voltages.

Voltage/V	Current in lamp/A	Current in wire/A
0.9	1.00	0.45
1.6	1.55	0.80
2.4	2.05	1.20
3.2	2.40	1.60
4.1	2.65	2.05
4.9	2.80	2.45

a) Use the same set of axes to draw graphs of current (y-axis) against voltage (x-axis) for the lamp and for the wire.

b) How does increasing the voltage affect the current in:
i) the lamp   ii) the wire?
If the current is proportional to the voltage, then doubling the voltage causes the current to double.

c) Use your graphs to find out if the current is proportional to the voltage for: i) the lamp   ii) the wire.

d) Describe how the resistance of the wire and the lamp changes as the voltage is increased.

Q3 a) Explain how it is possible to connect a number of low-voltage lamps safely to the mains supply.

b) How many 20V lamps should be connected to a 240V supply so that they light normally? Draw a circuit diagram of a suitable arrangement.

Q4 The table shows the current in nichrome wire when the length of wire is varied while the voltage remains constant.

a) Plot a graph of current (y-axis) against length of wire (x-axis) used.

b) Describe the pattern that the graph shows.

c) It is suggested that the current in the wire is inversely proportional to the length of wire used. Use data from the graph to test this hypothesis.

Length of wire/cm	Current/A
15.2	2.92
24.6	1.81
32.7	1.36
39.5	1.13
45.3	0.98
53.4	0.83

4–5 Electrical resistance

■ Resistance is the opposition to electric current. It is measured in ohms (Ω) and calculated using the formula:
$$R = V/I$$
■ The resistance of a metallic conductor has a constant value provided that the temperature stays the same. As the temperature increases, so does the resistance.
■ A diode is a component that allows current to pass in one direction only. Its symbol includes an arrow which shows the direction in which current can pass.
■ The resistance of thermistors and light-dependent resistors (LDRs) depends on environmental conditions. The resistance of a thermistor decreases with increasing temperature and that of an LDR decreases when the illumination increases.

Q1 Use the resistance equation to complete the table.

Voltage/V	Current/A	Resistance/Ω
15	3	
	0.5	12
240		400
12	0.3	
	6	15
20		0.15

Q2 The diagram shows a circuit for a resistance meter.

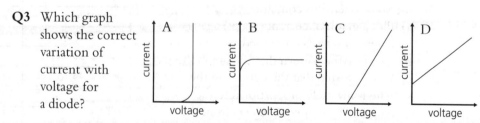

   a) Calculate the current that the ammeter shows when an object with a resistance of 100 Ω is placed between the probes.
   b) Calculate the current that the ammeter shows when the probes are touched together.
   c) Explain the purpose of the 10 Ω resistor.
   d) The resistance meter has two ranges. When set to the other range, it uses a 15V battery instead of a 1.5V battery. When would it be an advantage to use the 15V battery? Explain your answer fully.

Q3 Which graph shows the correct variation of current with voltage for a diode?

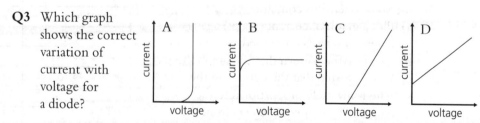

Q4 The three statements describe a light-dependent resistor (LDR), a thermistor and a diode. Match each statement to the correct component.

A Its resistance increases when the temperature decreases.

B Its resistance depends on the illumination.

C It only allows current to pass in one direction.

Q5 The table shows the current in a thermistor at different temperatures.

Temperature/°C	0	12	21	35	47	61
Current/A	0.016	0.022	0.028	0.043	0.067	0.120
Resistance/Ω						

The voltage remained constant at 6.0 V.

a) Calculate the resistance of the thermistor at each temperature.

b) Plot a graph of resistance (y-axis) against temperature (x-axis).

c) Describe how the resistance changes as the temperature of the thermistor increases.

d) Use the graph to determine the resistance of the thermistor at 25°C.

e) Is it true to state that 'if the temperature of the thermistor is doubled, its resistance halves'? Use data from the graph to justify your answer.

Q6 Three identical heaters are used to heat equal volumes of water which are initially at the same temperature. Each heater is connected in series with a diode. The diagrams show the circuits used.

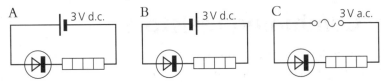

The heaters are left in the water for ten minutes. Explain why each water sample is at a different temperature after this time.

Q7 The table shows the results of an experiment to measure the current in a pencil lead (a mixture of graphite and clay) for different values of the voltage across it.

Voltage/V	1.5	3	4.5	6
Current/A	0.2	0.45	0.82	1.5

a) Calculate the resistance of the pencil lead for each pair of values of current and voltage.

b) Describe how the resistance changes when the voltage is increased.

c) Plot a graph of voltage against current. What do you notice about the slope of the graph?

d) It is possible that the change in resistance of the pencil lead was due to it getting hotter. Describe how you could test this idea.

Q8 The circuit shows how a light-dependent resistor can be used with other components to make a light meter, a device that measures light intensity. The resistance of the LDR is 250 Ω in bright sunlight and 2500 Ω in darkness.

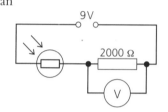

The total resistance of the circuit is 2250 Ω in bright sunlight and 4500 Ω in darkness.

a) Calculate the current in the circuit in each case.

b) Calculate the voltage across the 2000 Ω resistor in each case.

c) An analogue voltmeter is used which has a range of 0–10 V and a linear scale. On a sketch of the voltmeter scale, show the readings for bright sunlight and darkness.

d) The circuit could be modified by measuring the voltage across the LDR instead of across the fixed resistor. On a sketch of the voltmeter scale, show the readings for bright sunlight and darkness for the modified circuit.

Q9 In which of these circuits does the lamp light?

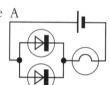 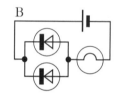 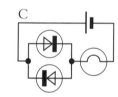

A1 Combining resistors

■ The formula for working out the effective resistance of two or more resistors connected in series is:
$$R_E = R_1 + R_2 + R_3 + \dots$$

■ The formula for working out the effective resistance of two or more resistors connected in parallel is:
$$\frac{1}{R_E} = \frac{1}{R_1} + \frac{1}{R_2} + \frac{1}{R_3} + \dots$$

■ A potential divider consists of two resistors in series. It subdivides the supply voltage into two smaller voltages.

Q1 Write down the resistance of each of the following series combinations.

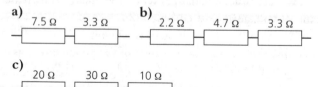

Q2 Calculate the resistance of each of the parallel combinations.

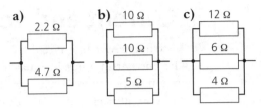

a) 2.2 Ω, 4.7 Ω
b) 10 Ω, 10 Ω, 5 Ω
c) 12 Ω, 6 Ω, 4 Ω

Q3 The circuit diagram shows three resistors in series with a power supply.
  a) Calculate the effective resistance of the circuit.
  b) Calculate the current in the circuit.
  c) Calculate the voltage across each resistor.
  d) Describe the link between the resistance of a resistor and the voltage across it in this circuit.

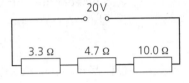

Q4 The circuit diagram shows three resistors in parallel with a power supply.
  a) Calculate the current in each resistor.
  b) Calculate the current at the points marked P, Q and R.
  c) Calculate the effective resistance of the circuit.

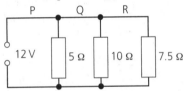

Q5 A heater is switched on and off by a transistor switch. It uses a temperature sensor made from a thermistor and a fixed resistor. The resistance of the thermistor decreases when the temperature increases. The circuit diagram shows the temperature sensor.
  a) Calculate the voltage across the 1000 Ω resistor when the voltage across the thermistor is 0.6 V.
  b) Use your value from **a)** to calculate the current in the circuit when the voltage across the thermistor is 0.6 V.
  c) Calculate the resistance of the thermistor when the voltage across it is 0.6 V.
  d) Suggest why the current in the sensing circuit needs to be low.
  e) Explain how the transistor switch turns the heater off when the temperature of the thermistor rises.

Q6 The diagram shows one way of drawing a potential divider circuit that is used for electronic switching.
Use the formula:
$V_{out} = V_{in} \times R_2/(R_1 + R_2)$
to calculate the output voltage for each line in the table.

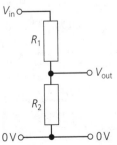

	V_{in}/V	R_1/Ω	R_2/Ω
a)	9	1000	1000
b)	9	100	1500
c)	12	100	2000
d)	12	15	210

6 Current and voltage

- Electric current in a circuit is a flow of charge.
- The current in amps is equal to the rate of flow of charge in coulombs per second. Current is calculated using the formula:

  current = charge flow ÷ time   or $I = Q/t$
- The energy transferred by the moving charge is measured by the voltage. One volt is an energy transfer of one joule for each coulomb of charge. Voltage is calculated using the formula:

  voltage = energy transfer ÷ charge   or $V = E/Q$

Q1 Which statement is correct?

A The current is 1 C when 1 A of charge flows past a point each second.
B The current is 1 A when 1 C of charge flows past a point each minute.
C The current is 1 A when 1 C of charge flows past a point each second.
D The current is 1 C when 1 A of charge flows past a point each minute.

Q2 Calculate the current in each of the following.
   a) 9 C of charge flow through a torch lamp in 60 s.
   b) 180 C of charge flow through a heater in 30 s.
   c) 300 C of charge flow through a car headlamp in one minute.
   d) 1.875×10^{16} electrons flow across an X-ray tube each second. The charge on each electron is 1.6×10^{-19} C.

Q3 The diagram shows a circuit for using an immersion heater from a low-voltage supply.
   a) Calculate the quantity of charge that flows through the heater in one minute.
   b) Write down the energy transfer in the heater by each coulomb of charge flowing through.
   c) Calculate the energy transfer in the heater in one minute.
   d) Calculate the energy transfer from the electricity supply in one minute.
   e) Explain why more energy is transferred from the supply than is transferred to the heater.

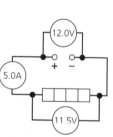

Q4 The energy transferred by charge flowing in a lamp is 30 J each second. The current is 0.25 A.
   a) What quantity of charge flows through the lamp in one second?
   b) Calculate the voltage across the lamp.

Q5 When a lamp is operating normally, the filament is very hot but the connecting wires remain cool.
   Use a model of charge flow to explain this.

7 Power in circuits

- Power is the rate of energy transfer in watts (W). 1 W is equal to 1 J/s. Power is calculated using the formula:

    power = energy transfer ÷ time   or $P = E/t$

- The power of a circuit component or electrical appliance depends on both the current and the voltage.
- The formula for electrical power is:

    power = voltage × current   or $P = V \times I$

Q1 Calculate the energy transfer in the following examples:
- **a)** a 1500 W hairdryer is used for 6 minutes
- **b)** a 2500 W kettle takes 4.5 minutes to boil some water
- **c)** a 2.5 W clock is working all day
- **d)** a 650 W microwave cooker takes 5 minutes to cook some food.

Q2 A gas burner has a power output of 1.25 kW (1250 W).
It takes 380 000 J of energy to boil 1 litre of cold water taken from a tap.
- **a)** Calculate the time it takes to bring the water to the boil.
- **b)** Give two reasons why it is likely to take longer than the time you have calculated in **a)**.

Q3 Complete the table.

Device	Current/A	Voltage/V	Power/W
hairdryer	6.5	230	
vacuum cleaner		230	880
headlamp	6	12	
radio	0.5	6	
security lamp		230	750

Q4 An electrical heater has a resistance of 500 Ω.
- **a)** Calculate the current in the heater when the voltage is 230 V.
- **b)** Calculate the power of the heater when the voltage is 230 V.
- **c)** Repeat the calculations of **a)** and **b)** when the heater is operated from a 115 V supply.
- **d)** Explain why, when the voltage is halved, the power does not halve.

Q5 Multi-way adaptors can be used to operate several mains appliances from one 230 V socket.
Explain why it is safe to operate a computer (150 W), monitor (350 W) and laser printer (470 W) from one of these adaptors, but it is not safe to use one to operate a kettle (2 500 W), fan heater (1 500 W) and an iron (1 400 W).

8–9 Electricity at home

■ There are three conductors in the mains supply to a house. The live wire carries the energy supplied to the house through electricity, the neutral wire is the return path for the current and the earth wire is a safety wire that is connected to the ground.

■ Fuses and circuit breakers protect fixed installation cables and flexible cables from overheating and possible fire risk.

■ The plug fuse together with the earth wire protect the user from electrocution.

■ Energy transfer in kilowatt-hours is calculated using the equation:

energy in kWh = power in kW × time in h

■ Domestic heaters often use a heating element which transfers its energy by conduction, convection or infrared radiation to the objects being heated.

Q1 The diagram shows part of the wiring to a desk lamp.
  a) Complete the diagram by joining the wires from the lamp to the correct terminals in the plug.
  b) Which wires have a current passing in them when the lamp is in normal use?
  c) The plug is fitted with a 1 A fuse. Explain why it would be dangerous to replace it with a 13 A fuse.
  d) What hazard does the earth wire protect against? Explain how it does this.

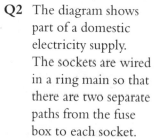

Q2 The diagram shows part of a domestic electricity supply. The sockets are wired in a ring main so that there are two separate paths from the fuse box to each socket.
  a) Which wires are switched by the main switch?
  b) In which connection is the fuse to the circuit?

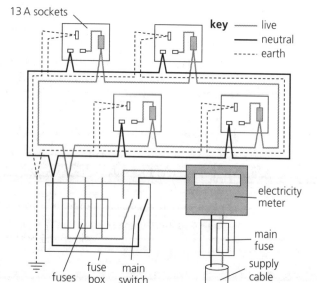

c) Draw a block diagram showing the energy flow from when it enters a house to when it arrives at a socket.

Houses used to be wired using radial circuits, where each socket had its own set of conductors wired to the fuse box. One advantage of a ring main is that it allows a current of up to 30 A with no more than 15 A passing in any conductor, since there are two current paths to each socket.

d) Explain why this is an advantage.

e) Suggest **two** further advantages of the ring main over radial circuits.

Q3 Complete the table, assuming that each kWh of energy from the electricity mains supply costs 8p.

Appliance	Power/kW	Time used/h	Energy transfer/kWh	Cost/p
hairdryer	1.6	0.3		
vacuum cleaner	0.88	0.75		
computer monitor	0.30	8.0		
kettle	2.5	1.5		

Q4 Microwave cookers transfer the energy from electricity into short wavelength radio waves which are absorbed by water and salt in the food being cooked. Domestic microwave cookers have an efficiency of 50% (50% of the energy from electricity is transferred to radio waves) and an output power of 650 W.

a) Calculate the power input when the microwave cooker is operating.

b) It takes twenty minutes to cook four large potatoes in a microwave cooker. Calculate the cost of doing this, taking the cost of energy to be 8p for each kWh.

The same potatoes take 1.20 hours to cook in a conventional oven which has a 2.5 kW heater. The heater takes 0.25 hours to warm the oven before the potatoes are put in and it is then switched on for one third of the cooking time to maintain the oven temperature.

c) Calculate the cost of cooking the potatoes in the conventional oven.

The cooking time when using the microwave oven depends on the amount of food being cooked, for the conventional oven the cooking time is the same for six potatoes as it is for one.

d) Under what circumstances could the cost advantage be in favour of the conventional oven?

Q5 Immersion heaters have a power of 2.5 kW. An immersion heater is left switched on overnight, from 7 pm to 7 am.

a) The cost of energy is 8p for each kWh. Calculate the cost of operating a 2.5 kW heater for 12 hours.

b) Explain why the cost of leaving an immersion heater on overnight is much less than the answer to **a)**.

c) A teenager falls asleep at 9 pm while reading a book in bed. She leaves her 40 W bedside lamp switched on until 6 am the following morning. How much does this add to the electricity bill at 8p for each kWhr?

Q6 The table shows how the maximum current rating of fixed installation cables depends on the cross-sectional area of the conductors.

a) Plot a graph of current rating (y-axis) against cross-sectional area (x-axis).

b) Describe the shape of the curve. Explain what this shows about how the current rating changes with cross-sectional area.

c) Is the current rating of cables directly proportional to cross-sectional area? Use data from the graph to justify your answer.

Cross-sectional area/mm²	Current rating/A
1.0	12
1.5	15
2.5	21
4.0	27
6.0	35
10.0	48

10–11 Static charge

■ When two materials are rubbed together, some charge in the form of electrons is transferred from one to the other.

■ Insulators do not allow charge to move through them, so charge on an insulator is 'static'.

■ Materials with the same type of charge repel each other. Materials with opposite types of charge attract each other.

■ When charge is allowed to build up, lightning and sparks can occur due to the air becoming ionised.

■ Static charge is used to do useful jobs in photocopiers, removing ash from power station waste gases, and in painting metal panels.

Q1 When a piece of glass is rubbed with polythene the glass becomes charged positively.

a) Explain how the glass becomes charged.

b) Draw a diagram to show the charge on the glass and the charge on the polythene.

Q2 The diagram shows what happens when some false 'hair' is placed on the dome of a van de Graaff generator, which is then charged.

a) Sketch a diagram to show the charge on the 'hair'.

b) Explain why the hair stands up when it is charged.

Q3 In a photocopier, an image is projected onto a charged rubber belt. The belt is coated with a material that is an insulator in the dark but conducts electricity when it is illuminated.
  a) Sketch the charges on the belt after the image has been projected.
The belt is then sprayed with a fine black powder.
  b) Explain why the powder sticks to some areas of the belt but not others.

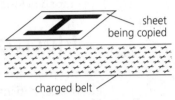

sheet being copied

charged belt

Before the powder can be transferred to a sheet of paper, the paper has to be charged.
  c) Explain why it is necessary to charge the paper.

Q4 The diagram shows a metal panel being sprayed with a positively charged powder.
  a) What type of charge does the panel acquire?
  b) Explain how the panel becomes charged.
  c) Describe the advantage of using charged powder to spray the panel.
  d) Explain how the painting process would be affected if there was no earth connection.

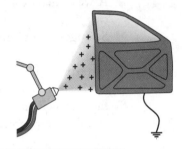

Q5 In a thundercloud, charge separation occurs. The bottom of the cloud becomes negatively charged, and the top of the cloud becomes positively charged.
  a) The Earth's surface normally has an excess of negative charge. Describe and explain how the presence of the thundercloud causes a change in the type of charge on the surface of the Earth.
A large voltage is created between the bottom of the thundercloud and the surface of the Earth.
This large voltage causes ionisation of the air particles.
  b) Describe what happens when air particles are ionised.
  c) Explain how ionisation of the air particles allows lightning (a large spark) to occur between the bottom of the thundercloud and the Earth.
When lightning passes between a cloud and a building, the result can be extensive damage to the building, and fire. The purpose of a lightning conductor is to prevent lightning occurring by discharging the cloud.
The diagram shows a lightning conductor on a church tower.
A large voltage is created at the tip of the

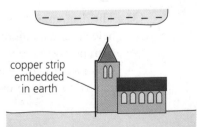

copper strip embedded in earth

conductor. This causes ionisation of the surrounding air, resulting in discharge of the base of the thundercloud.

d) Explain how the tip of the lightning conductor becomes charged.

e) Explain how ionisation of the air can discharge the base of the thundercloud.

12 Electromagnetism

■ All electric currents have their own magnetic field – this is called electromagnetism.

■ A weak magnetic field exists inside and around a coil of wire that is carrying a current.

■ Stronger fields can be created by wrapping the coil around an iron core.

■ Electromagnets consisting of a coil of wire wrapped on an iron core are used in relays for switching.

■ Electric bells use an electromagnet linked to a 'make-and-break' circuit to repeatedly switch an electromagnet on and off.

Q1 An electromagnet is made by wrapping a coil of wire around a paper core and connecting the coil to a battery.
Which of the following would increase the strength of the electromagnet?
A Using stronger paper.
B Using an iron core.
C Increasing the battery voltage
D Using fewer turns of wire on the coil.

Q2 Diagram A represents four compasses placed around a single wire passing into the paper. No current passes in the wire.
a) Explain why all the compasses point in the same direction.
b) In diagram B the current has been switched on. Add arrows to show which way the other three compasses point.

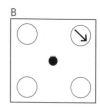

Q3 The diagram shows part of the magnetic field around a coil of wire that has a current passing in it.
Complete the diagram to show the field pattern in and around the coil.

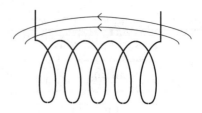

Q4 A relay is an electromagnetic switch that is operated when a small current passes in the coil.
   a) Write down **one** use of a relay.
   b) Describe **two** reasons for using a relay to switch an electric current.

Q5 The diagram shows an electric bell.
   a) Describe the sequence of events when the bell push is operated.
   b) Describe and explain the effect of turning the contact screw one turn clockwise.

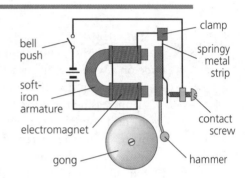

13 The d.c. motor

■ There is a force exerted on a current-carrying wire in a magnetic field.
■ The force is at right angles to both the wire and the magnetic field.
■ An electric motor consists of a coil of wire placed within a magnetic field. Rotation is caused by the turning effect of the forces on the sides of the coil.
■ In a d.c. motor, connections to the coil are made by a split–ring commutator. This reverses the current in the coil once each half revolution so that the coil keeps turning in the same direction.

Q1 Which set of arrows shows the relative directions of the current, magnetic field and force on a wire correctly?

Q2 a) Match the name of each part of an electric motor to its job.

Part	Job
coil	provides the magnetic field
brush	reverses the current in the coil
commutator	rotates
fixed magnets	passes current to the commutator

b) Label the parts of the motor
in **a)** on the diagram.

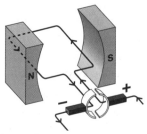

Q3 The diagram shows how you can investigate the
force on a wire in a magnetic field.
a) Write down the effect of:
i) increasing the current
ii) decreasing the current
iii) reversing the current direction
iv) reversing the direction of the magnetic field.
b) Explain why it is not possible for the force on
the wire to be in the same direction as the current.

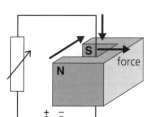

Q4 The diagram shows part of a simple motor.
a) Explain how rotation of the coil is caused by
the action of **two** forces acting on it.
b) Draw the forces acting when the coil has
turned through one quarter of a revolution
so that its plane is vertical.
c) Explain why the forces acting in **b)** do not cause rotation.
d) Explain why practical motors have several coils of wire wound on
the armatures.

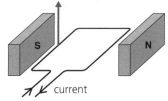

14 Electromagnetic induction

■ A voltage is induced in a conductor whenever the magnetic field
around it changes. If there is a complete circuit, the induced voltage
causes a current to pass in the conductor.
■ The size of the induced voltage depends on the rate at which the
magnetic field changes.
■ Reversing the change causes the direction of the induced voltage to
be reversed.

Q1 The diagram shows equipment that can be used to
show the principles of electromagnetic induction.
a) Describe how you could use this equipment to
demonstrate that:
i) a voltage is induced in a conductor whenever
the magnetic field around it changes

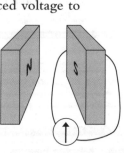

ii) the size of the induced voltage depends on the rate at which the magnetic field changes

iii) reversing the change causes the direction of the induced voltage to be reversed.

b) Apart from the speed of movement, what other factors affect the size of the induced voltage?

Q2 The diagram shows a bicycle dynamo.
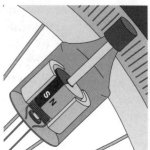
a) Explain how the dynamo generates electricity.
The dynamo generates an alternating current.
b) Describe the difference between alternating current and direct current.
c) One disadvantage of dynamos is that the lights go out when the bicycle stops. Explain why this happens.
d) Describe and explain **two** changes to the alternating current when the bicycle increases speed.

Q3 In a foundry, metal objects are manufactured by pouring molten metal into moulds. To melt the metal, solid bars are placed in a heat-resistant container that is then placed inside a coil of wire. When a high-frequency alternating current passes in the coil, the metal becomes heated and melts.

a) Explain how electromagnetic induction causes the metal to become heated.
b) Suggest why a high-frequency alternating current is more effective than a low-frequency alternating current.

A2 Storing and retrieving information

■ Compact discs store information in digital form. Magnetic tape can store information in either analogue form or digital form.

■ A moving-coil microphone uses electromagnetic induction to make an electrical copy of a sound signal.

■ A loudspeaker uses electromagnetism to produce sound when an alternating current passes in it.

Q1 Which option describes the difference between digital and analogue signals correctly?

A Digital signals can have both positive and negative values, but analogue signals are always positive.

B Digital signals can vary continuously, but analogue signals can only have certain values.

C Analogue signals can vary continuously, but digital signals can only
have certain values.

D Digital signals can only be used for speech, but analogue signals can
also represent music.

Q2 The diagram shows a playback head used in a tape
recorder. As the magnetised tape passes over the
narrow gap, it causes an alternating current to pass
in the wire coil.

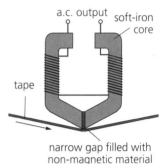

a) Explain how the movement of the magnetic
tape causes a current in the coil.

b) What **two** factors determine the frequency of
the current in the coil?

c) What **two** factors determine the size of the
current in the coil?

Q3 The diagram shows a moving-coil microphone.

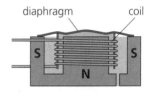

a) Explain how speaking into the microphone
causes an electric current with the same
frequency as the sound to pass in the wire coil.

b) What change takes place to the electric current
when the amplitude of the sound changes?

Q4 The diagram shows the arrangement of the coil and the
permanent, cylindrical magnet in a loudspeaker.

a) In which direction is the force on the coil when the
current in the coil is:

   i) clockwise?

   ii) anticlockwise?

b) Describe and explain the movement of the coil when
an alternating current with a frequency of 1500 Hz passes in the coil.

c) Explain how variations in the current in the coil enable the
loudspeaker to reproduce sounds of varying loudness.

15 Transformers

■ Transformers can change the size of an alternating voltage by having
different numbers of turns of wire on the primary and secondary coils.

■ The relationships between the voltages, power and currents in the
coils are given by the formulae:

$$\frac{V_p}{V_s} = \frac{N_p}{N_s} \qquad V_p I_p = V_s I_s \qquad \frac{I_p}{I_s} = \frac{N_s}{N_p}$$

Q1 The diagram shows two separate coils of wire. One coil is connected in
series with a cell and a switch. The other coil is connected to a sensitive,
centre-zero ammeter. When the current in the
left-hand coil is switched on, the ammeter needle
moves to the right, and then back to zero.

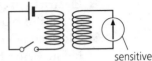

sensitive
ammeter

a) Explain why the ammeter needle moves.

b) Explain why the ammeter needle returns to zero.

c) Describe and explain what happens to the ammeter needle when the
current in the left-hand coil is switched off.

d) Describe and explain the effect of placing the coils on an iron core.

Q2 Use the transformer
formulae to
complete the table.

Number of turns on primary coil	Number of turns on secondary coil	Primary voltage/V	Secondary voltage/V
100	250	6	
1000	100		230
	3000	12	230
350		230	4600
3000		230	20
1000	2	230	
2000	200000	2500	
	400	450	15

Q3 A step-up transformer increases the 230 V mains to 5000 V.

a) Calculate the ratio $\dfrac{\text{number of primary turns}}{\text{number of secondary turns}}$

b) Calculate the current in the primary when the secondary current
is 0.5 A.

c) State **two** differences between the primary and secondary windings.

Q4 The diagram shows a solder gun. It is a step-down transformer with a
single-turn secondary winding.
When the voltage across the primary coil is
240 V, the primary current is 0.6 A and the
induced voltage in the secondary coil is 2.0 V.

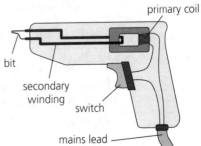

primary coil

bit

secondary
winding

switch

mains lead

a) Calculate the number of turns of wire on
the primary coil.

b) Calculate the current in the secondary
winding.

c) Explain why the secondary winding is
made from a thick aluminium rod.

d) Suggest why the 'bit', the part that becomes very hot, is thinner than
the rest of the secondary winding.

16 Power transmission

■ Electricity is generated at power stations by electromagnets rotating in coils of wire.

■ Alternating current at 25 000 V goes into a step-up transformer before being fed into the national grid.

■ The national grid transmits power at a high voltage in order to minimise the current and keep power losses as small as possible.

■ Transformers are used to reduce the voltage before the electricity is supplied to consumers.

Q1 The diagram represents part of the national grid.

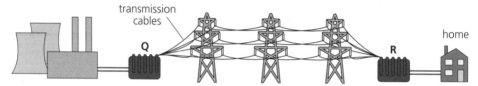

a) At which part of the diagram is the voltage:
  i) the highest?   ii) the lowest?

b) The electrical power input to transformer Q is at 25 000 V. Write down **two** ways in which the output from Q is different to the input.

c) What is the purpose of transformer R?

d) Not all of the electrical power output from transformer Q reaches transformer R. Describe what happens to the power that is 'lost'.

Underground cables can be used instead of overhead ones. Underground cables have to be cooled by pumping oil through them.

e) Explain why it is not necessary to pump oil through overhead cables to keep them cool.

f) In what circumstances are underground cables preferred to overhead ones?

g) Suggest why the company that operates the national grid prefers to install overhead cables rather than underground ones.

Q2 On the national grid, power is transmitted at a high voltage to minimise the current.

a) Explain why it is an advantage to minimise the current.

Electricity is generated at 25 000 V and then stepped up to 400 000 V as it leaves the power station.

b) Suggest **one** reason why the electricity is not generated at 400 000 V.

c) Calculate a suitable turns ratio for the step–up transformer.

d) Explain why electrical power is generated and distributed using alternating current rather than direct current.

Q3 In a power station generator, an electromagnet rotates 50 times each
second inside three sets of copper coils.
The generator produces 500 MW at 25 000 V.
a) Calculate the total current being generated.
b) Calculate the current in each coil.
c) Explain why the coils are made from thick strips of copper rather
than copper wire.
d) At times of peak demand, the load on the generator causes the
frequency of rotation of the electromagnets to drop. Explain how
this affects both the voltage and the frequency of the output from
the generator.
e) Some electric clocks and other machines rely on the frequency of
the mains supply for accuracy. Suggest why the electromagnets in
generators are often rotated at a higher frequency at night.

A3 Logical systems

■ An electronic system has an input, a processor and an output.
■ Logic gates are processors. The name of each gate describes how the
output depends on the inputs.
■ A latch is an example of a bistable circuit. It maintains its output
after the input has been removed.

Q1 The table shows an incomplete truth table.
Draw up complete truth tables for each of the
following gates:
   i) AND   ii) OR
   iii) NAND   iv) NOR.

Inputs		Output
0	0	
1	0	
0	1	
1	1	

Q2 Many cars contain an electronic
circuit which sounds a buzzer if the
door is opened while the car
headlights are on. The diagram
shows part of the circuit used.
a) Why is the driver given a warning
when the car door is opened
while the headlights are on?
b) Name the logic gate shown in
the diagram.
c) Copy and complete the table.

from headlight   logic gate
                                    buzzer
from sensor in door

Headlight	Door	Buzzer (on or off)
off	closed	
on	closed	
on	open	
off	open	

Q3 The security lock on a shop safe is controlled by three keys. The shop manager keeps and uses only key **M**, the deputy manager key **D** and the chief cashier key **C**. When a key is inserted into its keyhole it causes the input to a logic gate to be 'on'. The diagram shows the circuit that is used.

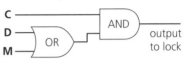

a) Copy and complete the table, using a 0 for 'off' and a 1 for 'on'.

b) Which line of the table shows what happens when the manager and his deputy try to unlock the safe?

	Inputs to OR gate		Input to AND gate		
	D	M	OR gate output	C	AND gate output
i)	1	1		0	
ii)	1	0		1	
iii)	0	1		1	
iv)	0	0		1	

c) Which line of the table shows what happens if the deputy manager and chief cashier try to unlock the safe?

d) The safe is unlocked when the output from the AND gate is '1'. Who needs to be present in order to unlock the safe?

Q4 A burglar alarm has two switches that can cause it to sound. One is fitted to each main door so that if either door is opened the alarm sounds. The diagram represents the electronic system used.

a) Which type of logic gate should be used?
b) Explain how the alarm becomes switched on.
c) Why is the latch necessary?
d) Why is the relay necessary?
e) What is the purpose of the latch input labelled **R**?

A4 Using transistors

- A transistor can be used as a current amplifier. The amplification is equal to:

  collector current ÷ base current   or $I_c \div I_b$

- A transistor can be used as a switch. It is 'on' when the base–emitter voltage is 0.7 V.

- Capacitors store charge. The greater the charge on a capacitor, the higher the voltage across it.

Q1 Which of the transistors shown in the diagram is conducting?

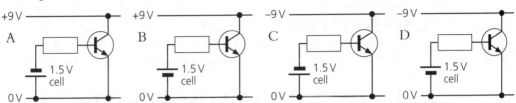

Q2 The base current of a transistor is 2 mA (0.002 A) when the collector current is 150 mA (0.150 A).
a) Calculate the emitter current.
b) Calculate the current gain of the transistor.

Q3 The diagram shows a circuit for investigating how the voltage across a capacitor changes with time.
The table shows the voltmeter readings taken at ten-second intervals after the switch is closed.

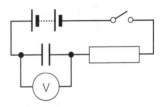

Voltage/V	0	1.63	2.97	4.06	4.96	5.69	6.29	6.78	7.18	7.51	7.78
Time/s	0	10	20	30	40	50	60	70	80	90	100

a) Plot a graph of voltage against time.
b) Use your graph to describe how the voltage across the capacitor changes as the capacitor charges.
The capacitor and the resistor are used in a time-delay circuit to switch on a transistor. The transistor is switched on when the voltage across the capacitor is 0.7 V.
c) What time elapses between switching on the circuit and the transistor becoming switched on?
d) Write down **two** ways of changing the circuit to increase the time-delay.

Q4 The diagram shows a circuit that can be used for switching on a lamp or other appliance when the surrounding light level fades.

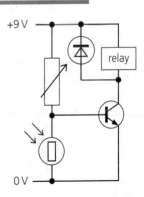

a) Identify the part of the circuit that is the:
  i) input sensor ii) processor iii) output.
b) Explain how reducing the illumination of the LDR causes the transistor to become switched on.
c) Why is a variable resistor used rather than a fixed resistor in the potential divider?
d) Explain why the transistor is used to switch a relay rather than switching the lamp directly.

e) Explain how the circuit could be modified to switch on an alarm at dawn.

f) Many shops have a 'counter' at the entrance to record the number of customers that enter the shop. Explain how this circuit could be used, along with other components, to make a suitable electronic system.

A5 The cathode ray oscilloscope

■ Cathode rays are high-speed electrons. They are produced when electrons emitted from a hot wire are accelerated using a high voltage.

■ The kinetic energy gained by an electron when it is accelerated through a high voltage is calculated using the formula:
$$E_k = e \times V$$

■ The voltage and frequency of an alternating voltage can be measured from a calibrated oscilloscope trace.

Q1 The diagram shows an electron gun, a device that produces cathode rays.

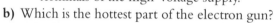

  a) Copy the diagram, and label:
    i) the cathode
    ii) the anode
    iii) the positive and negative terminals of the high–voltage supply.
  b) Which is the hottest part of the electron gun?
  c) Which part of the gun gives off electrons?
  d) Which part of the gun accelerates and focuses the electrons?

Q2 The electronic charge, e, is 1.6×10^{-19} C.
  a) Calculate the kinetic energy of an electron that has been accelerated through 4000 V.
  b) High-energy electrons can produce X-rays when they are stopped by hitting a target. Suggest why the screens in television tubes and oscilloscopes are made of glass that contains lead.

Q3 The diagram on the next page shows the trace on an oscilloscope screen when an alternating voltage is applied to the input.
The time-base is switched on and the setting is 5 ms/cm.
The y-sensitivity is 10 V/cm.
  a) What is the maximum voltage shown by the trace?
  b) What is the minimum voltage shown by the trace?
  c) Calculate the frequency of the alternating voltage.

d) Sketch the appearance of the trace when the speed of the time–base is doubled.

e) Sketch the appearance of the trace when the time–base is switched off.

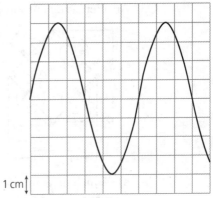

1 cm↕

A6 Rectification and smoothing

■ When an alternating voltage is applied to a diode, the diode only conducts on half of the cycle.

■ A single diode produces a half-wave rectified direct current from an alternating current. Four diodes can be used to produce a full-wave rectified direct current.

■ The rectified direct current produced by a diode can be smoothed by using a capacitor connected in parallel with the load.

Q1 Here are four oscilloscope traces.

a) Which trace shows a half-wave rectified direct voltage?

b) Which trace shows a full-wave rectified direct voltage?

c) Which trace could have been obtained by connecting a battery to the oscilloscope?

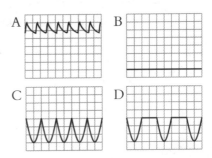

Q2 The diagram shows the effect of a smoothing capacitor on a half-wave rectified direct current.
The capacitor has been omitted from the diagram.

a) Where in the circuit should the capacitor be connected?

b) Sketch the trace obtained when a larger value capacitor is used.

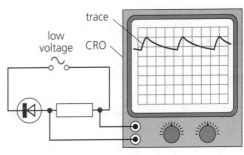

c) Sketch the trace obtained when a smaller value load resistor is used with the original capacitor.

d) Describe how the capacitor smoothes the half-wave rectified current.

Q3 An alternating current can be full-wave rectified by using four diodes.

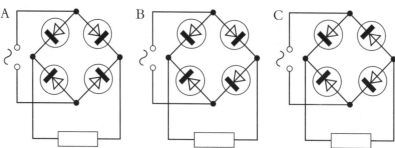

a) Which diagram shows a circuit that can be used for full-wave rectification?

b) In which direction is the current in the resistor when the polarity of the a.c. supply is:
   i) positive at the upper terminal in the diagram?
   ii) negative at the upper terminal in the diagram?

c) Draw the trace that would be on the screen of an oscilloscope connected in parallel with the resistor, assuming the time-base is switched on.

d) Draw the trace on the oscilloscope when the full-wave rectified direct current is smoothed by using a capacitor.

e) Explain how the smoothness of the trace obtained depends on the value of the capacitor used.

B Forces and motion

17 Changing shape

■ All materials stretch when subjected to a pulling force, but some stretch more than others.

■ A material is elastic if it returns to its original size and shape when the force is removed. A material is plastic if it undergoes permanent deformation.

■ Some materials, such as metals, behave in a regular and predictable way when they are subjected to small forces – their extension is proportional to the force applied.

■ These materials are said to obey Hooke's law, which states that the extension is proportional to the force, provided that the limit of proportionality is not exceeded.

Q1 The graphs show how the extension changes with the stretching force for four different materials.
  a) Which two graphs show materials that follow Hooke's Law?
  b) Which two graphs show materials that become less stiff as they are stretched?
  c) Which graph shows a material that maintains the same stiffness?

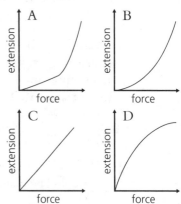

Q2 The table shows the results of increasing the force on a stretched steel wire.

Force/N	10	20	30	40	50	60	70	80	90	100
Extension/mm	0.7	1.4	2.1	2.8	3.5	4.2	5.1	6.2	7.4	8.7
Does it return to its original size when the force is removed?	yes	yes	yes	yes	yes	yes	yes	yes	no	no

  a) Use squared paper to plot a graph of force against extension.
  b) For what range of forces does the steel obey Hooke's law? Explain how you can tell.
  c) For what range of forces is the steel elastic? Explain how you can tell.
  Another sample of steel has the same diameter but is half the length.
  d) Add a line to your graph to show the pattern of behaviour when this wire is subjected to the same stretching force.
  e) The steel wire is used to suspend a 100 N weight without stretching the steel beyond its elastic limit. Explain how this can be done.

Q3 Car tyres are made of rubber, a stretchy material.
  a) Explain why the 'tread' of a car tyre, the part that makes contact with the road, needs to be stretchy.
  b) Does the tread need to be elastic? Give a full explanation to support your answer.
  c) Explain the advantage of making the tyre wall from a stiff material.

18–19 Using pressure

- Forces can have different effects according to the area they act over. The effect a force has in piercing or cutting depends on the pressure it exerts.
- Pressure is calculated using the formula:
$$\text{pressure} = \frac{\text{force}}{\text{area}} \quad \text{or} \quad p = F/A$$
- Pressure can be measured in N/cm^2 or N/m^2. The pascal (Pa) is an alternative name for N/m^2.
- Liquid pressure acts equally in all directions. This enables the pressure to be transmitted round corners and through flexible pipes.
- Liquids are used to magnify forces in braking systems and machinery where large forces are used to move things.

Q1 Hard cheese is a difficult material to cut through. The diagram shows cheese being cut with a wire.
Explain why it is easier to cut the cheese with a wire than with a knife.

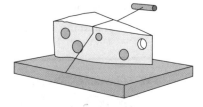

Q2 A person who weighs 750 N sits in a chair that weighs 150 N. There are four chair legs on the ground; the area of contact between each chair leg is $3\,cm^2$.
  a) Calculate the pressure exerted on the ground by each leg.
  b) Explain how the pressure changes when the person leans back so that two legs lose contact with the ground.
  c) Suggest how some floor coverings can be damaged by people who lean back while sitting in chairs.

Q3 Use the pressure formula to complete the table.

Force/N	Area force acts over/m²	Pressure/Pa
150 000	30	
	0.0005	275
240		3000
	6.5	250 000
3 000 000	0.5	

Q4 Which **two** statements are correct?

A Liquids and solids transmit pressure in all directions.

B Liquids transmit force but solids transmit pressure.

C Liquids transmit pressure but solids transmit force.

D Liquids exert pressure in all directions.

Q5 The diagram represents part of a hydraulic press, a machine used for shaping metal panels.

A force of 250 N acts on a small piston that has an area of 6 cm².

a) Calculate the pressure caused by this force.

b) Write down the pressure transmitted by the oil.

c) Calculate the area of the large piston if the oil pushes it with a force of 10 000 N.

d) Write down **two** advantages of using hydraulics in machines such as a hydraulic press.

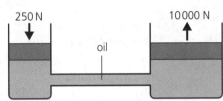

Q6 The diagram shows part of a hydraulic jack, a device used to lift cars and other vehicles when a tyre is being changed.

a) Explain how a small force on the small piston causes a much greater force at the large piston.

The area of the small piston is 3 cm² and that of the large piston is 45 cm². A force of 600 N is needed to lift the front wheels of a van.

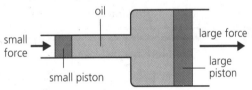

b) Calculate the force needed at the small piston to lift the van.

In lifting the van, the large piston moves a distance of 25 cm.

c) Calculate the distance moved by the small piston.

20 How fast?

■ The speed of a moving object is calculated using the formula:

$$\text{average speed} = \frac{\text{distance travelled}}{\text{time taken}} \quad \text{or} \quad v = \frac{s}{t}$$

■ Speed can also be calculated as the gradient of a distance–time graph.

■ Displacement describes the distance of an object from a certain position. Displacement can be positive or negative, the different signs showing opposite directions.

■ The gradient of a displacement–time graph represents the velocity of the moving object. Like displacement, velocity can be positive or negative depending on the direction of travel.

Questions for Unit 20

Q1 Use the speed formula to complete the table. Take care to give the correct unit with each of your answers.

Distance travelled	Time taken	Average speed
150 m	7.5 s	
2160 km	3 hours	
5.7 cm	0.3 s	
	2.7 s	14.5 cm/s
350 km		80 km/hour
100 m	12.6 s	
	180 s	3.2 m/s
	0.25 hours	15 km/hour
0.5 m		10 m/s
1500 m		2.5 m/s

Q2 Here is a distance–time graph for part of a car journey.
a) For how long was the car stationary?
b) Calculate the speed of the car at each of the sections labelled **A, B, C** and **D** on the graph.
c) Calculate the average speed during the 45 s time interval.

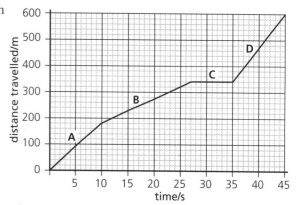

Q3 Here is a displacement–time graph for a train in a shunting yard.

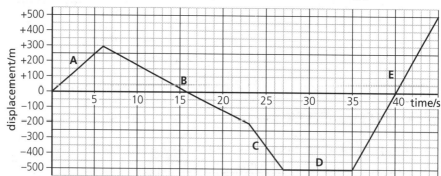

a) What was the furthest distance the object moved from its starting point?
b) At which times shown on the graph did the object return to its starting point?
c) At which labelled part of the graph was the object not moving? Explain how you can tell.
d) Calculate the velocity of the object at the parts of the graph labelled **A** and **B**. Explain how you can tell that these represent travel in opposite directions.

21–2 **Stopping and starting**

■ The distance a vehicle travels while braking depends on several factors – the state of the driver is important, as are the road conditions and those of the tyres and brakes.

■ All drivers take time to react to a changing situation. While they are reacting, their vehicle carries on moving.

■ The 'stopping distance' of a vehicle is made up of both the 'thinking distance' and the 'braking distance'.

■ Whether a moving object changes its speed depends on the balance of the forces that are acting.

■ Balanced forces cause no change. The object either continues to be stationary or travels in a straight line at constant speed.

■ If the forces acting on the object are unbalanced there is a change of speed. The speed increases if the force causing motion is greater than the resistive forces acting and decreases if the resistive forces are greater.

Q1 A driver notices a hazard in the road and brakes the vehicle. The graph shows how the speed of the vehicle changes after the driver notices the hazard.

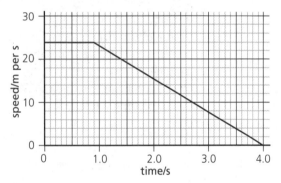

a) What was the speed of the driver when the hazard was first noticed?

b) What time elapsed between the driver noticing the hazard and applying the brakes?

c) State **three** factors that could affect this 'thinking time'.

d) Calculate the 'thinking distance', the distance that the vehicle travelled before the brakes were applied.

e) How long did it take for the vehicle to brake to a halt?

f) The average speed of the vehicle while braking was 12 m/s. Calculate the braking distance.

g) State **three** factors that affect the braking distance of a vehicle.

h) Calculate the stopping distance of the vehicle.

i) Sketch a graph to show how the speed of the vehicle would have varied if the vehicle had been travelling at 15 m/s when the driver noticed the hazard.

Q2 The data in the table are taken from the highway code. They show how thinking distance and braking distance are related to the speed of a car, in mph.

Speed/mph	Thinking distance/m	Braking distance/m
20	6	6
30	9	14
40	12	24
50	15	38
60	18	55
70	21	75

  a) Use the data to draw a graph of thinking distance against speed.

  b) Describe the shape of your graph line. Does it show that thinking distance is proportional to speed? Explain how you can tell.

  c) Use the data in the table to plot a graph of braking distance against speed.

  d) Describe the shape of the graph line that you drew in **c)**.

  e) Use data from your graph to describe what happens to the braking distance when the speed of a car is doubled.

Q3 The diagram shows the horizontal forces acting on a car travelling at a steady speed on a level road.

  a) Label the force arrows 'resistive force' and 'driving force'.

  b) Explain why the arrows have been drawn the same length.

  c) Draw arrows to represent the forces acting on the car when the car is:
    i) accelerating while travelling on a level road
    ii) braking while travelling on a level road.

Q4 The graph shows how the speed of a cyclist changes in the first few seconds of a cycle ride.

  a) Explain why the graph is steepest as the cyclist sets off.

  b) Describe what happens to the size of the forces acting as the cyclist speeds up.

  c) At which part of the graph are the forces on the cyclist balanced? Explain how you can tell.

Q5 **a)** Use the data in the table in **Q2** to draw-up a table showing how the stopping distance of a car depends on its speed.

  b) Draw a graph of stopping distance against speed.

  c) What advice would you give to a driver who habitually drives at 50 mph in a built-up area? Use data from your graph to support your argument.

It has been suggested that the speed limit in built-up areas should be reduced from 30 mph to 20 mph.

  d) Use the data from your graph to suggest how effective this would be in reducing the number of pedestrians killed on roads each year.

B1 Floating and sinking

■ Density is calculated using the formula:
   density = mass ÷ volume
■ When an object floats the vertical forces acting on it are balanced.
■ An object can only float if its overall density is less than that of the surrounding fluid.

Q1 Use the density formula to complete the table.

Material	Mass	Volume	Density
concrete		$4.0\,m^3$	$2500\,kg/m^3$
glass	$84\,g$	$35\,cm^3$	
gold	$25\,g$		$19\,g/cm^3$
air		$12\,m^3$	$1.1\,kg/m^3$
petrol	$24.8\,g$	$30.2\,cm^3$	

Q2 A sample of rubber has a mass of $21.6\,g$. When it is lowered into a measuring cylinder containing water, the water level rises from $57\,cm^3$ to $89\,cm^3$.
   a) Write down the volume of the rubber.
   b) Calculate the density of the rubber.

Q3 Young children who are learning to swim sometimes use an expanded polystyrene 'float'. The diagram shows a piece of expanded polystyrene floating on water.

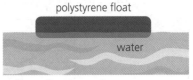
polystyrene float

water

   a) Draw arrows to show the two forces acting on the polystyrene.
   b) Write a description of each force acting on the polystyrene.
   c) A child sits on the polystyrene float. The float sinks further into the water. Explain how this sinking enables the float to support the weight of the child.

Q4 Sea water has a density of $1100\,kg/m^3$.
   Fresh water has a density of $1000\,kg/m^3$.
   A small ship has a mass of 25 000 tonnes (1 tonne = 1000 kg).
   When floating, the ship displaces its own weight of sea water.
   a) Calculate the volume of sea water displaced by the ship.
   When the ship floats, 40% of it is submerged.
   b) Calculate the volume of the ship.
   c) Calculate the overall density of the ship.
   When the ship sails into a freshwater canal the water level on the side of the ship changes.
   d) Describe and explain the change that occurs.

23–4 Acceleration

■ Acceleration is defined as being the increase in velocity ÷ time taken and is measured in m/s^2 or ms^{-2}.

■ Acceleration can also be calculated as the gradient of a speed–time or a velocity–time graph. If a speed–time graph has a negative gradient this represents a deceleration.

■ A negative gradient on a velocity–time graph represents either a deceleration or an acceleration in the direction of negative velocity.

■ A moving object can only change its velocity if the forces on it are unbalanced.

■ If the forces on an object are unbalanced, its acceleration depends on the size of the unbalanced force and its mass:

$$\text{force} = \text{mass} \times \text{acceleration}$$

Q1 Calculate the acceleration of:
a) a car that speeds up from 0 m/s to 27 m/s in 9.6 s
b) a milk float that accelerates from 2.3 m/s to 3.7 m/s in 4.5 s
c) a bicycle that starts from rest and reaches a speed of 12.3 m/s after 6.5 s
d) an aircraft that accelerates from 50 m/s to 135 m/s in 12.5 s.

Q2 Here is a speed–time graph for part of a car journey.

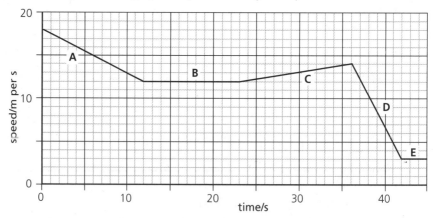

a) Describe the motion that the graph represents.
b) Which sections of the graph show no acceleration? Explain how you can tell.
c) Calculate the acceleration represented by the other sections of the graph.
d) Calculate the distance travelled during each section of the graph.
e) Use your answer to **d)** to calculate the average speed over the 45 s that the graph represents.

Q3 The diagram shows the driving force on a car as it sets off from rest.
The total mass of the car is 900 kg.
a) Calculate the initial acceleration of the car.
b) Explain why the acceleration decreases as the car speeds up.

1200 N

In normal braking, the car decelerates at $2.5\,\text{m/s}^2$.
c) Calculate the braking force required.
When going on holiday, the driver puts the luggage on a roof rack.
d) Explain how this extra load is likely to affect the acceleration of the car.
e) Explain how it is likely to affect the braking of the car.

Q4 Before taking off, a hot-air balloon is fastened to the ground using ropes.
The 720 kg balloon weighs 7200 N. The gas jet is fired and the ropes are discarded when the upward force reaches a value of 8000 N.
a) Calculate the initial acceleration of the balloon.
Shortly after take-off, the pilot discards 100 kg of ballast.
b) Explain how this affects the acceleration of the balloon.

Q5 In which of the following examples are the forces on the moving object unbalanced?
A   A car maintaining a constant speed as it turns a corner.
B   A train braking as it approaches a station.
C   A milk float travelling at a constant 3 m/s along a level road.
D   A sky-diver falling at terminal velocity.

Q6 Seat belts and crumple zones are designed to reduce the injuries to passengers when cars collide.
In a 'mock' collision a car is fitted with a dummy driver. The dummy is made to simulate a human being to test the car's safety features. The car decelerates at $600\,\text{m/s}^2$ from a speed of 30 m/s.
a) Calculate the time taken to stop the car.
b) Explain why a dummy that is not fitted with a seat belt is likely to be extensively damaged.
When the dummy is fitted with a seat belt and the 'collision' is repeated, the dummy decelerates at $150\,\text{m/s}^2$.
c) Calculate the time taken to stop the dummy.
d) Explain how it is possible for the car and the dummy to take different times to stop.

e) Suggest why it is not desirable for the deceleration of the dummy to be reduced further by adjusting the seat belt.

f) The dummy has a mass of 65 kg. Calculate the force required to stop the dummy and suggest possible effects of this force on a human-like dummy.

g) A second car is made to crumple when it collides, extending the collision time to 0.6 s. Explain how this is likely to reduce damage to the dummy in the collision.

Q7 Here is a velocity–time graph for a car journey.

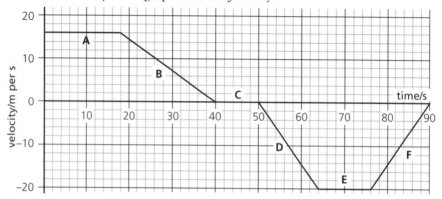

a) What change in the motion takes place after the first 50 s shown on the graph?

b) How long did the car spend at rest?

c) How long did the car spend travelling at constant speed?

d) Which section of the graph shows the car speeding up?

e) Which two sections of the graph show the car slowing down?

f) Calculate the value of the acceleration for each lettered section of the graph.

g) Calculate the distance travelled during each lettered section of the graph.

h) Calculate the average speed of the car during the 90-second time interval that the graph represents.

25 Falling down

■ Gravitational forces act between any two objects that have mass. The Earth pulls you and you pull the Earth with an equal-sized force in the opposite direction.

■ Close to the Earth's surface, the strength of the Earth's gravitational field is 10 N/kg, meaning that each kg of mass is pulled down with a force of 10 N.

■ The downward pull of the Earth is called an object's weight. It is calculated using the formula:

weight = mass × gravitational field strength

■ When an object falls freely with no resistive forces acting, the Earth's pull causes a downwards acceleration of $10 \, m/s^2$.

Q1 Two apples are placed side-by-side on a table with a 1 cm gap between them.
Which is the correct explanation of why they stay apart?
A There is no gravitational force between the apples.
B The Earth's gravitational pull on the apples is bigger than the attractive force between the apples.
C The gravitational forces on each apple cancel out.
D Friction between the apples and the table stops them from moving together.

Q2 The gravitational field strength on the Moon's surface is 1.5 N/kg.
a) Calculate the weight of a 60 kg person on the surface of the Earth and on the surface of the Moon.
An astronaut walking on the Moon has to wear a space suit and carry his own oxygen supply.
b) Explain why he still finds it easy to walk, despite having the extra mass to carry.
One of the first 'experiments' done on the Moon was to release a hammer and a feather at the same time.
c) Write down **two** ways in which the vertical motion differed from that in a similar experiment done on Earth.

Q3 The table shows the total distance travelled by a freely-falling object in the 5 s after it is released.

Time/s	0	1	2	3	4	5
Total distance travelled/m	0	5	20	45	80	125

a) Use the data to plot a graph of distance travelled (y-axis) against time taken (x-axis).
b) Describe the shape of the curve.
c) Read from your graph the time taken to travel:
  i) 50 m
  ii) 100 m.
d) Explain why the time taken to travel 100 m is not twice as long as the time taken to travel 50 m.

Q4 The value of free-fall acceleration can be measured
by taking a series of photographs of a falling object. The
diagram shows the results of photographing a falling ball.
The time interval between successive photographs is 0.1 s.
During the first 0.1 s, the ball travelled a distance of
4.8 cm or 0.048 m (measured from the diagram).
a) Calculate the average speed of the ball in the first 0.1 s.
As the acceleration is uniform and the ball started from
rest, the final speed can be worked out as twice the
average speed.
b) Using the initial and final speeds, calculate a value for
the acceleration of the ball in the first 0.1 s.
c) Calculate the acceleration of the ball during the first:
i) 0.2 s   ii) 0.3 s   iii) 0.4 s.
d) Use your answers to **b)** and **c)** to calculate an average
value for the free-fall acceleration of the ball. Suggest
why your calculations give a value that is less than the
accepted value.

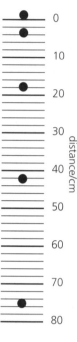

26 Turning forces

■ The turning effect, or moment, of a force depends on the
perpendicular distance to the pivot as well as the size of the force.
■ How effective a force is at causing rotation is measured by its
moment. The moment is calculated using the formula:
  moment = force × perpendicular distance to pivot
■ The forces acting on a static object must not only be balanced in
each direction – their turning effects, or moments, must also balance.
■ This is known as the principle of moments, which states that when
an object is in equilibrium the sum of the clockwise moments about
any pivot is equal to the sum of the anticlockwise moments.

Q1 In a large building such as a school or office block, internal doors must
be kept shut to reduce the risk of fire spreading. A fire door requires a
moment of 60 Nm to open it. The diagrams show five forces applied to
the door.

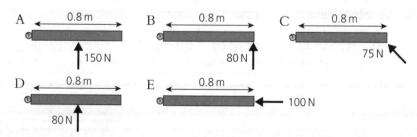

a) Which of the five forces would open the door?

b) Which of the five forces has no turning effect?

Q2 Calculate the force, F, needed to open the trapdoor in the diagram.

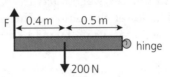

Q3 A pair of scissors being used to cut paper is an example of a lever that magnifies force.

a) Write down **two** other examples of levers being used to magnify force.

b) Write down **one** example of a lever being used to magnify movement.

The total force applied at each handle of the scissors shown in the diagram is 80 N.

c) Calculate the size of each force acting on the paper.

d) Explain how the size of the force on the paper changes as the scissors cut through it.

e) How can the person using the scissors maintain a constant cutting force as scissors cut through the paper?

Q4 A decorator rests a plank on two supports. The plank is 4.0 m long and the supports are placed symmetrically 2.0 m apart.
The weight of the plank acts from its centre.
The decorator weighs 750 N.
The decorator stands to the right of the right-hand support.

a) Calculate the furthest distance from the support that he can stand without causing the plank to tip.

b) What additional weight should he place at the centre of the plank to enable him to stand safely at the right-hand edge of the plank?

c) Calculate the minimum distance between the supports so that there is no danger of the plank tipping when the decorator walks on it.

B2 How stable?

■ An object's weight acts from its centre of mass.
■ The lower the centre of mass, the more stable an object is.
■ Stability is also affected by the width of an object's base.

Q1 The diagrams show some everyday objects.

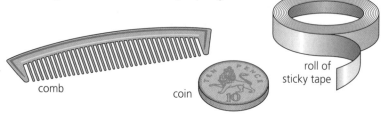

Draw diagrams to show the weight force that acts on each object.

Q2 The diagram shows two cans of drink. One is full and the other is only half full.
  a) Draw the weight force that acts on each can.
  b) Which can is more stable? Explain why this can is more stable.

Q3 A glue-stick is stood on its base. Use a diagram to explain why it is likely to fall over if it is accidentally knocked.

Q4 The diagram shows equal volumes of liquids placed in a measuring cylinder, a beaker and a conical flask.
  a) Which is the most stable? Explain why it is the most stable.
  b) Which is the least stable?
  c) What design feature of the least stable container is an attempt to improve its stability?

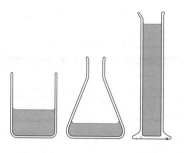

Q5 A 65 kg cyclist rides a 15 kg cycle.
    a) On a diagram, estimate the position of the centre of mass and explain why the combination of cycle and cyclist could topple when turning a corner.
    b) Explain why a motorcyclist on a motorcycle is more stable than a cyclist on a cycle.

B3–B4 Momentum

■ All moving objects have momentum. Momentum is calculated using the formula:
$$\text{momentum} = \text{mass} \times \text{velocity}$$
■ When two objects interact the total momentum stays the same provided that there are no other forces involved.
■ The change in momentum caused by a force acting on an object is called the impulse. It is calculated using the formula:
$$\text{impulse} = \text{change in momentum} = \text{force} \times \text{time}$$
■ Conservation of momentum applies to rocket and jet propulsion. The change in momentum of the exhaust gases from a rocket is balanced by an equal change in momentum of the rocket in the opposite direction.

Q1 Calculate the momentum of each of the following:
    a) a 10 000 kg bus travelling at 15 m/s
    b) a 10 g bullet travelling at 400 m/s
    c) a 500 000 kg jumbo jet cruising at 300 m/s.

Q2 In foggy conditions on a motorway vehicles travelling in the same direction can collide and stick together. A 30-tonne lorry travelling at 25 m/s hits the back of a 20-tonne lorry travelling at 15 m/s.
    a) Calculate their common speed after the collision.
    b) If it had been a head-on collision, what would the speed after the collision have been?

Q3 A balloon is blown up but the neck is not tied.
Explain why the balloon is propelled forwards when it is released.

Q4 A golf ball has a mass of 46 g (0.046 kg). It is hit by a golf club with an average force of 50 N. The club and ball are in contact for a time of 0.05 s.
    a) Calculate the change in momentum of the ball.
    b) Calculate the speed of the ball as it leaves the club.
    c) What effect does hitting the ball have on the speed of the golf club?
    d) Explain why the change in speed of the golf club is much smaller than that of the golf ball.

Q5 In films at the cinema and on television, people who have been 'shot' are often shown reeling backwards.
Use your answer to **Q1b)** to calculate the speed of a 60 kg person, initially at rest, after being hit by a bullet.

Q6 When tennis players and cricketers hit a ball, they often attempt to maintain contact between the bat and the ball for as long a time as possible.
Explain the advantage of prolonging the contact time between the bat and the ball.

Q7 In an air-track 'collision' between two vehicles fitted with repelling magnets, a 0.1 kg vehicle approaches a stationary 0.2 kg vehicle at a speed of 0.3 m/s.
The 0.1 kg vehicle rebounds with a speed of 0.1 m/s.
Calculate the speed and direction of the 0.2 kg vehicle after the collision.

Q8 A rocket burns fuel at the rate of 13 000 kg each second. The exhaust gases have a speed of 2500 m/s. The rocket is travelling in space, out of the influence of gravitational fields.
a) Calculate the change in momentum of the exhaust gases in 1 s.
The rocket has a mass of 2700 tonnes (1 tonne = 1000 kg).
b) Calculate its change in speed each second.
The rocket continues to burn fuel at the same rate.
c) Explain why its acceleration increases as more fuel is burned.

B5 Equations of motion

■ The equations of motion apply to any movement where the acceleration is uniform. The four equations are:

$$v = u + at \qquad\qquad v^2 = u^2 + 2as$$
$$s = ut + \tfrac{1}{2}at^2 \qquad\qquad s = \tfrac{1}{2}(u+v)t$$

■ Projectiles move both horizontally and vertically. The horizontal motion is at constant speed. The equations of motion apply to the vertical (accelerated) motion.

Q1 Calculate the acceleration of a car that increases speed from 12.5 m/s to 26.5 m/s in 8.5 s.

Q2 In a famous car advertisement, a car is driven over the edge of the roof of a building.
The height above the ground is 5.5 m. Free-fall acceleration is 10 m/s².

a) Calculate the time it takes for the car to reach the ground.

b) Calculate the vertical speed of the car as it hits the ground.

As the car leaves the roof, it is travelling horizontally at 15 m/s.

c) How far is it from the wall of the building when it hits the ground?

Q3 An archer fires an arrow horizontally at a target that is 60 m away.
The horizontal speed of the arrow as it leaves the bow is 75 m/s.

a) Calculate the time that the arrow is in the air.

b) Free-fall acceleration is 10 m/s^2. Calculate the vertical distance travelled by the arrow while it is in the air.

c) How should the archer compensate for this vertical motion?

Q4 A cyclist travelling at a speed of 12 m/s brakes and decelerates at 2.5 m/s^2.

a) How long does it take for the cyclist to stop?

b) Calculate the distance that the cyclist travels while braking.

If the braking force is doubled, the cyclist's deceleration is 5.0 m/s^2.

c) Does this cause the braking distance to halve? Justify your answer by showing appropriate calculations.

Q5 A rope is held vertically above the ground.
It has some weights tied to it.
When the rope is released the weights make a series
of 'clunks' as they hit the ground. These 'clunks'
are spaced at equal time intervals.
The bottom weight is 0.50 m above ground level
before the rope is released.
Calculate the height of the next three
weights above ground level.

C Waves

27–8 Wave reflections

- A reflection of a sound wave is called an echo.
- The total distance travelled between a sound being emitted and its echo received can be calculated using the formula:
  $$\text{distance} = \text{speed} \times \text{time}$$
- Echoes of ultrasound (high frequency sound) are used at sea and in medicine.
- We see objects when the light from a light source is reflected into our eyes.
- Most surfaces reflect light in all directions.
- When light is reflected by a mirror surface the angles of incidence and reflection are equal.
- The image formed by a mirror is virtual, upright and the same distance behind the mirror as the object is in front.

Q1 People who live near airports often fit double glazing to reduce the amount of noise entering their houses.
Explain why less sound passes through a double-glazed window than through a single-glazed one.

Q2 Ships and submarines use SONAR to detect other objects under the water. A pulse of sound is sent into the water and any echoes are then detected.
A ship sends out a sound pulse and detects the echo from a submarine 25.6 s later.
In sea water sound travels at 1500 m/s.
a) Calculate the distance of the submarine from the ship.
b) How certain can the ship's captain be about the precise distance between the ship and the submarine?

Q3 If you turn all the lights out on a dark evening you can see to watch television but not to read a book.
Explain how 'seeing' a television picture is different from 'seeing' a book.

Q4 The diagram shows a person using a mirror to look at his chin.
a) Draw a line to show how light from his chin reaches his eye.
b) Mark a 'C' in the position of the image of his chin.
c) Explain why a person standing behind the mirror cannot see the image.
d) If his chin is 15 cm from the mirror, what is the distance between his chin and its image?

Q5 It is possible, using a sheet of glass as a mirror, to place a piece of paper in a candle flame without it burning. The diagram shows how it is done.

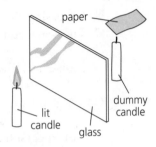

  a) Whereabouts is the dummy candle positioned?
  b) Explain why the dummy candle appears to be lit.
  c) If you were doing this as a 'trick', where would you position your audience?

Q6 Bats use ultrasound to 'see' their prey. They send out short pulses and then detect the reflections.

The speed of sound in air is 330 m/s.

  a) If an insect is 1.0 m from a bat, what time elapses between the bat sending the pulse out and receiving the reflection?
  b) Explain why the bat cannot be certain precisely where the insect is.
  c) Bats use ultrasound to make other measurements, apart from where the insect is. What other measurements does the bat need to make to be certain of catching its prey?

Q7 Air-traffic controllers use RADAR to detect aircraft in the air. A pulse of radio waves is sent out and any reflections are detected. The radio waves travel in air at 3×10^8 (300 000 000) m/s.

  a) An aircraft is 10 000 m from an airport. What time elapses between the pulse being emitted and its echo being received?
  b) How certain can the air-traffic controllers be of the precise position of the aircraft?

29–30 Wave measurements

■ Sound is produced by vibration and is transmitted through substances as a longitudinal wave. The particles vibrate along the direction of wave travel.

■ Surface water waves and electromagnetic waves such as light and radio waves are transverse wave motions. The vibrations are at right angles to the direction of wave motion.

■ The loudness of a sound changes when the amplitude of the vibrations changes. The amplitude is the greatest displacement from the normal position.

■ The wavelength, λ, of a wave motion is the length of one complete cycle of a wave – that is, a compression and rarefaction for a longitudinal wave; a crest and a trough for a transverse wave.

■ The frequency, f, is the number of vibrations each second.

■ Increasing the frequency of a sound wave increases the pitch.
■ The wave equation:

$$\text{speed} = \text{frequency} \times \text{wavelength} \quad \text{or} \quad v = f\lambda$$

applies to all waves.

Q1 A glass harmonica is a musical instrument that consists of glasses containing water. When the rim of a glass is rubbed, it makes a sound.
   a) Suggest how a sound is made when the rim of the glass is rubbed.
   b) Suggest how the note made by a particular glass can be changed.
   c) Describe how the sound travels from the harmonica to a listener's ear.

Q2 Classify each of the following waves as either longitudinal or transverse:
   a) radio
   b) X-ray
   c) ultrasound
   d) a pulse of waves used for measuring the depth of the seabed
   e) microwaves used in cooking.

Q3 Here are three sources of sound:
   a) drum   **b)** radio   **c)** piano
   For each of the above sound sources:
      i) identify the part that vibrates
      ii) state how the amplitude of vibration can be changed.

Q4 The graph represents the movement of an air particle transmitting a sound wave.
   a) Mark a distance that represents the amplitude of the wave.
   b) To the same scale, sketch a graph to show the movement of the air particle when the loudness is increased.

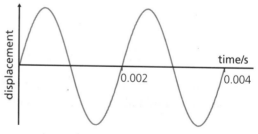

   c) Write down the time taken for one complete vibration to take place.

Q5 A young person can detect sounds with frequencies in the range 20 Hz to 20 000 Hz.
   a) What is the frequency of the highest pitched sound that can be heard? The speed of sound in air is 330 m/s.
   b) Calculate the wavelength in air of the lowest pitched sound that the person can detect.

Q6 The diagram represents a transverse wave travelling along a rope.

a) How many wavelengths are shown on the diagram?

b) Write down the values of:
    i) the amplitude of the wave
    ii) the wavelength of the wave.

The speed of the wave on the rope is 1.5 m/s.

c) Calculate the frequency of the wave.

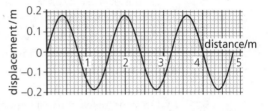

Q7 Use the wave equation to work out the quantities a) to f).

Wave speed / m per s	Frequency / Hz	Wavelength / m
a)	225	1.80
b)	2.50	1200
350	c)	0.12
2500	d)	3.60
330	1.20	e)
2500	0.15	f)

Q8 In an ultrasound scan the same crystal that produces the waves is used to detect the reflections.

A short pulse of ultrasound at a frequency of 1.5 MHz ($1\,MHz = 1 \times 10^6\,Hz$) has a duration of 1.0×10^{-5} s.

a) How many wavelengths does the pulse consist of?

b) The speed of ultrasound in the body is around 1500 m/s, depending on the tissue. Calculate the wavelength of the ultrasound at this speed.

c) A reflection of the pulse is detected after a time of 1.6×10^{-4} s. Calculate the depth of the tissue that reflected the sound.

d) Explain why the ultrasound pulses used for body scans need to be of short duration.

C1 Resonance

■ All objects have a natural frequency of vibration.

■ Forcing an object to vibrate at its natural frequency results in large-amplitude vibrations – this is called resonance.

Q1 The table shows the results of an experiment to find out how the natural frequency of a mass–spring system depends on the mass on the spring.

Mass/kg	0.1	0.2	0.3	0.4	0.5	0.6	0.7	0.8
Natural frequency/Hz	2.91	2.05	1.68	1.45	1.30	1.19	1.10	1.03

a) Describe how to measure the natural frequency of an oscillating mass on a spring.

b) Use the data in the table to draw a graph of natural frequency (*y*-axis) against mass (*x*-axis).

c) Describe the shape of the graph line.

d) What does this tell you about the way in which the natural frequency changes with increasing mass?

e) Use your graph to find the mass needed to make the spring oscillate with frequencies of: i) 1.25 Hz   ii) 2.5 Hz.

f) Do your answers to e) support the view that 'doubling the mass on the spring causes the natural frequency to halve'? Give the reason for your answer.

Q2 A manufacturer of dishwashers built machines that resonated when in normal operation. The solution to the problem was to fit concrete blocks to the machines.

a) Explain why resonance of the machines was a problem.

b) Explain how fitting the concrete blocks stopped the machines from resonating when in normal operation.

c) Under what circumstances could the machines that had been fitted with concrete blocks resonate?

Q3 The outer ear resonates at a frequency of around 3000 Hz.

a) Explain why a sound at the natural frequency of the outer ear sounds louder than a sound with a different frequency but the same amplitude.

b) Why would you expect the precise value of the outer ear's natural frequency to vary from person to person?

Q4 Different parts of the body have different natural frequencies. The natural frequency of an eyeball is higher than that of a lung.

a) Explain why an eyeball has a higher natural frequency than that of a lung.

Resonance of the eyeball can be a danger to helicopter pilots.

b) Suggest how resonance could be caused in the eyeball of a helicopter pilot.

c) Explain why such resonance can be a danger.

d) What should a helicopter pilot do if she is aware that her eyeballs are resonating?

C2 Sound and music

■ The natural frequency of an instrument depends on the length of the string or air column that vibrates.

■ Whole-number multiples of the natural frequency are called harmonics.

■ The quality, or timbre, of a note depends on which harmonics are present and their amplitudes.

Q1 Middle C has a frequency of 256 Hz.
Which of the following are harmonics of middle C?
A 64 Hz   B 128 Hz   C 512 Hz   D 1024 Hz.

Q2 The diagram represents a stretched
string vibrating at its natural
frequency of 312 Hz.

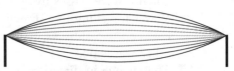

    a) Sketch the appearance of the string when vibrating at each of the
first three harmonics.

    b) Write down the frequency that each mode of vibration in **a)**
corresponds to.

    c) Which of these frequencies does the string vibrate at when it is
plucked in the middle?

Q3 The table shows the results of an experiment to investigate how the
natural frequency of a vibrating air column depends on its length.

Length of air column/m	0.17	0.28	0.40	0.52	0.67	0.81
Natural frequency/Hz	485	295	205	160	125	100

    a) Describe how you could investigate the relationship between the
length of air column and the natural frequency.

    b) Plot a graph of natural frequency (y-axis) against length of air
column (x-axis).

    c) Use your graph to find the length of air column that has a natural
frequency of: i) 200 Hz   ii) 250 Hz.

    d) Refer to your answers to **c)** and the data in the table.
Can you conclude that the length of air column and natural
frequency are in inverse proportion? In other words doubling one
causes the other to halve. Obtain more data from the graph to
support your answer.

Q4 The speed of sound in air is 330 m/s.

    a) Use the data in **Q3**, which refers to a column closed at one end, to
derive data showing how the wavelength of the sound from the air
column depends on its length.

    b) Plot a graph of wavelength against length of column.

    c) Analyse your graph to find the relationship between the length of a
closed air-column and the wavelength of the natural frequency.

31 Refraction of light

■ Refraction is the name given to the change in speed that occurs when a wave passes from one substance into another.

■ Waves travelling in a direction at right angles to the boundary between two substances do not change their direction, but all other waves do.

■ The change in direction is towards the normal line (a line drawn at right angles to the boundary) when waves slow down and away from the normal line when waves speed up.

■ Virtual images are sometimes formed when light is refracted.

Q1 Which diagram shows the correct change in direction when light passes from glass into air?

Q2 Which line in the table gives the correct change in frequency, speed and wavelength when light passes from glass into air?

	Frequency	Speed	Wavelength
A	increases	decreases	unchanged
B	increases	increases	increases
C	unchanged	decreases	decreases
D	unchanged	increases	increases

Q3 Complete the diagrams, showing what happens to the waves when light passes from water into air.

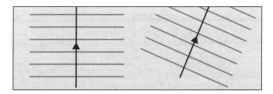

Q4 Objects viewed through water appear to be nearer than they really are. The diagram shows light that has been reflected from a fish in a tank of water.

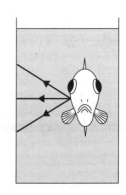

  a) Complete the diagram by showing the path of the light in the air outside the tank (ignore the effects of refraction through the glass).

  b) Trace back the lines you drew in **a)** to locate the image of the fish.

  c) An observer looking into the tank would focus on the image of the fish. Choose **three** words or phrases from the list that describe the image.

  **diminished   inverted   magnified   real   same size
  upright   virtual**

Q5 The diagram shows a party trick that uses refraction.
Place a coin inside an opaque container and seat an observer so that the coin is just obscured by the wall of the container. When water is poured into the container, the observer can see the coin.
Explain how this effect is caused by refraction.

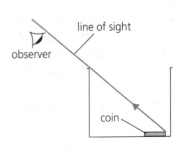

32 Using TIR

■ Light travelling from glass or water into air does not always pass through the boundary.
■ When light hits the boundary below the critical angle, some is reflected and the rest passes through.
■ At angles of incidence greater than the critical angle, about 42° for glass, all the light is reflected internally.
■ Total internal reflection (TIR) is used in prisms to turn light round corners and in fibres for communication and endoscopy.

Q1 In which of these circumstances could total internal reflection occur?
A light passing from air into glass
B light passing from water into glass
C light passing from glass into water
D light passing from water into air.

Q2 Prisms can be used to turn light through 90° or 180°.
a) Complete the diagram to show how the prism turns the light through 90°.
b) Draw a diagram showing how the prism could be used to turn light through 180°.
c) Write down three examples of prisms being used to turn light through 90° or 180°.

Q3 The critical angle for a water–air surface is 49°.
a) Draw diagrams to show what happens to light meeting a water–air surface at angles of: i) 30°   ii) 45°   iii) 50°.
A man and his child are swimming under water.

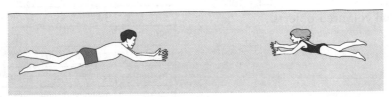

b) The man can see his child and an image of the child. Explain how the image of the child is formed.

c) As they swim towards each other, the image disappears. Explain why the man cannot see an image when they are close together.

Q4 The diagram shows light passing along a glass fibre. The fibre is surrounded by air.

The speed of light in glass is 2.0×10^8 m/s and the speed of light in air is 3.0×10^8 m/s.

a) Explain why the light that hits the glass–air boundary is totally internally reflected.

While being handled, part of the fibre gains a thin coating of grease. The speed of light in the grease is 1.95×10^8 m/s.

b) Describe and explain what happens when light hits the glass–grease surface.

The fibres used in endoscopes and for transmission of data have an outer cladding.

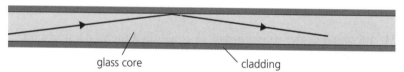

glass core   cladding

c) Explain why use of the cladding results in all the light staying in the fibre, even if the outside becomes coated with grease or any other substance.

33 Colour

■ White light is a mixture of all the colours.
■ A triangular prism can be used to disperse white light into a spectrum.
■ Colour televisions work by colour addition. The three primary colours, red, green and blue, are mixed to produce all the other colours.
■ Colour filters and coloured objects take colours away from the light.
■ The table shows which primary colours are subtracted by filters and coloured objects.

Colour of filter or object	Primary colours transmitted or reflected	Primary colours subtracted
red	red	green and blue
green	green	red and blue
blue	blue	red and green
yellow	red and green	blue
magenta	red and blue	green
cyan	green and blue	red

Q1 Choose the statement that completes the following sentence correctly.
White light is dispersed by a prism because:
A the frequency of the light increases as it enters the prism
B the frequency of the light decreases as it enters the prism
C the colour of each frequency changes as the light enters the prism
D different frequencies change speed by different amounts as they enter the prism.

Q2 A colour television screen is coated with three phosphors, which are materials that give out light when hit by electrons moving at a high speed. The three phosphors each emit a different primary colour.
a) Write down the colours that the phosphors emit.
b) Explain how a part of the screen can look to be:
i) yellow   ii) white   iii) orange.

Q3 When white light passes through a magenta filter followed by a cyan filter, blue light emerges.
a) Explain what has happened to the other colours that were present in the white light.
b) Which combination of two secondary colour filters only transmits red light?
c) Mixing coloured paints has the same effect as using colour filters together. Explain why mixing cyan and yellow paint gives green but mixing cyan and yellow light on a white screen gives an off-white.

Q4 Stage lighting uses colour filters to make objects appear different colours.
a) Write down two ways in which green scenery could be made to appear black.
b) Explain why it is not possible to make green scenery appear red.
c) Suggest one advantage of painting scenery using secondary colours rather than primary colours.

Q5 All shades of colour can be printed on white paper using just the three secondary colours. Colour photographs use three thin layers of colour, each of which acts like a filter.
Which colours need to be present on a section of photograph that is:
a) black?   **b)** blue?   **c)** red?

C3 Changing direction

■ Refractive index is a measure of the change in speed when light passes from air into a transparent material. It is calculated using the formula:

$$\text{refractive index} = \frac{\text{speed of light in vacuum}}{\text{speed of light in material}}$$

Questions for Unit C3

■ A convex lens causes parallel light to converge. A concave lens causes parallel light to diverge.
■ The principal focus of a lens is the distance from the centre of the lens to the image position for a parallel beam of light.

Q1 The table gives the values of the refractive index of some materials.

Material	Refractive index
water	1.33
glass	1.50
diamond	2.42
ice	1.30

a) In which of these materials does light travel with the greatest speed?

b) Which material causes the greatest speed change when light enters it from the air?

c) In air, light travels at 3.0×10^8 m/s. Calculate the speed of light in ice and in diamond.

d) A pond has a layer of ice on top. Is it possible for light that passes through the ice to undergo total internal reflection at the ice–water surface? Explain your answer fully.

Q2 The speed of light in salt is 1.94×10^8 m/s. Use the speed of light in air from **Q1** to calculate the refractive index of salt.

Q3 Complete the diagrams to show the effect that a concave lens could have on light that is:
A diverging
B parallel
C converging.

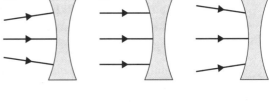

Q4 Complete the diagrams to show the effect that a convex lens could have on light that is.
A diverging
B parallel
C converging.

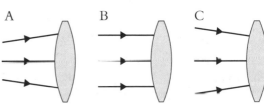

Q5 The refractive index of glass depends on the frequency. The refractive index for blue light is greater than that for red light.
The diagram shows light from a white object arriving at a convex lens.
The path of blue light is shown after refraction at the lens surface.

a) Use a diagram to show the refraction of green light and red light by the lens.

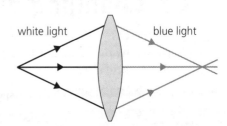

b) A white screen is placed at the image position for blue light. Describe the appearance of the image on the screen.

c) Explain why this lens would not give good results if used in a camera to take colour photographs.

C4 Using lenses

■ Convex lenses are used to form real images in cameras and projectors.
■ A magnifying glass uses a convex lens to form a virtual image.
■ Convex lenses in eyes focus the image onto the retina.

Q1 The diagram shows a camera being used to take a photograph of a person. Light from a point on the person's head is shown being focused on the film.

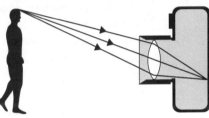

a) Write down **three** words or phrases that describe the image.

b) Draw a diagram to show where the image is formed when the person moves closer to the camera.

c) Explain how the camera is adjusted to focus on the closer person. A camera lens has a focal length of 50 mm.

d) What is the shortest distance from the lens that an object can be placed for the lens to form a real image?

e) Explain why most camera lenses of focal length 50 mm cannot be focused on an object less than 0.3 m away.

Q2 **a)** Complete the diagram to show how a convex lens acts as a magnifying glass.

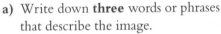
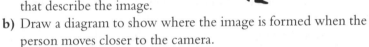

object

b) Write down **three** words or phrases that describe the image.

c) Explain how the size of the image changes when the object is moved closer to the lens.

Q3 The diagrams illustrate a short-sighted eye and a long-sighted eye. Explain how these defects can be corrected by using lenses. You should use diagrams to illustrate your answer.

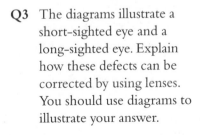

light from a distant object

short sight

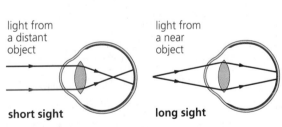

light from a near object

long sight

Q4 The diagram shows the main features of an eye.
Describe the function of **each** of the labelled parts.

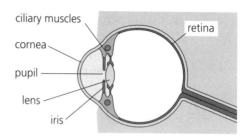

34 A family of waves

■ The electromagnetic spectrum is a family of transverse waves ranging in wavelength from less than 1×10^{-12} m (a millionth of a millionth of a metre) to thousands of metres.
■ The shortest waves are X-rays and gamma rays, followed by ultraviolet and then light.
■ Waves longer than light are infrared, microwaves and radio waves.
■ Diffraction is the spreading out of waves when they pass an obstacle or go through a gap.
■ The greatest spreading occurs when the size of the gap is the same as the wavelength of the waves. Very little spreading occurs at gaps which are many wavelengths wide.

Q1 Here are four types of wave from the electromagnetic spectrum.
   A ultraviolet   B infrared   C microwave   D radio
   a) Which of these waves has the shortest wavelength?
   b) Which has the greatest frequency?
   c) Which is emitted by all objects, no matter what their temperature is?

Q2 Our eye–brain system interprets waves as colours.
Which option gives the factor that determines the 'colour' of light?
   A the wavelength
   B the speed
   C the amount of diffraction
   D the frequency.

Q3 **a)** Explain why long wavelength radio waves are readily diffracted, but X-rays are not.
   b) Describe the dangers caused by exposure to waves with a wavelength shorter than that of light.

Q4 Mobile telephones communicate using radio waves. Satellites are used to transmit calls between countries. The diagram on the next page shows how dish aerials are used to focus a beam of radio waves and transmit it to a satellite. This minimises the effects of diffraction.

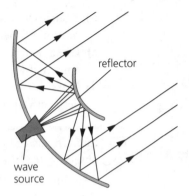

a) Explain why it is important to minimise the effects of diffraction.

b) What **two** factors determine the amount of diffraction that takes place when a wave passes through an opening?

c) The radio waves used for satellite transmission have a much shorter wavelength than the 0.30 m used by the mobile telephones.
Suggest why 0.30 m is unsuitable.

C5 Interfering waves

■ Interference occurs whenever two or more waves cross – it is readily observed by using two sources that are vibrating in step.

■ Constructive interference occurs when the displacements of both waves are in the same direction – the result is a wave with increased amplitude.

■ Destructive interference occurs when the displacements of the waves are in opposite directions, causing a reduction in the amplitude.

Q1 The diagram shows a person standing in front of two loudspeakers that are vibrating in phase.
The person is the same distance from each loudspeaker.

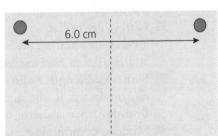

a) Explain why the person detects a loud sound.

b) The person walks along the dotted line. Describe the change in the sound detected as the person walks along the line.

c) The frequency of vibration of the loudspeakers is now increased. Explain how this affects the sound detected as the person walks along the line.

Q2 The diagram represents two dippers placed 6.0 cm apart in a ripple tank. They are made to vibrate in step so that they generate surface water waves that have a wavelength of 2.0 cm.

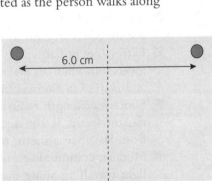

a) Explain why you would expect to observe constructive interference at points along the dotted line.

b) A small float is placed at a point on the dotted line. Describe the motion of the float.

c) Use a sketch to mark other lines where you would expect to observe constructive interference.

d) Mark on your sketch lines where you would expect to see destructive interference.

Q3 Interference of light is difficult to observe. One of the difficulties is obtaining two sources vibrating in step. This can be overcome by using diffraction.

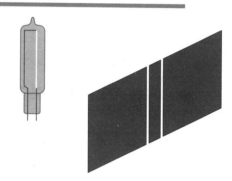

Two scratches are made close together on a blackened glass microscope slide. The slide is then illuminated by placing a single lamp at a distance of about 1 metre.

a) Explain why the waves reaching the slide are indistinguishable from plane (straight) waves.

b) Draw a diagram to show the waves emerging from the scratches on the slide. Mark on your diagram lines of constructive and destructive interference.

c) What would you expect to observe at positions of constructive interference and at positions of destructive interference?

d) The wavelength of green light is 0.5 μm. Use your diagram to explain why it is difficult to distinguish between the positions of constructive and destructive interference.

35–6 Waves and communications

■ Microwaves are short wavelength radio waves which are absorbed by water and salt molecules in food, causing heating.

■ Infrared radiation has a wavelength shorter than that of microwaves but longer than light. It also causes heating when absorbed by objects.

■ Ultraviolet radiation has a wavelength shorter than that of light. It is given out when an electric current passes through mercury vapour and is used in fluorescent tubes for lighting.

■ Short wavelength radio waves are used to transmit information in a narrow beam. Radio and television broadcasts use waves ranging from less than a metre to hundreds of metres.

■ Modern communications systems transmit information with pulses of light travelling along optical fibres.

Q1 Which list shows ultraviolet, microwave and infrared radiation in the correct order of increasing frequency?

    A ultraviolet   infrared   microwave

    B infrared   ultraviolet   microwave

    C microwave   infrared   ultraviolet

    D infrared   microwave   ultraviolet.

Q2 Hot bacon and tomato rolls can be bought at a train buffet. They are pre-packed in expanded polystyrene containers and reheated using a microwave cooker.

    a) Explain why the microwaves do not heat the expanded polystyrene container.

    b) Suggest why the contents of the reheated roll are hotter than the bread roll itself.

    Microwaves and infrared radiation are both used in cooking.

    c) Explain how the properties of microwaves make them more suitable than infrared for reheating food.

Q3 All objects emit infrared radiation, but the intensity and range of wavelengths emitted depend on the temperature of the object. Describe **two** uses of infrared cameras and explain why an optical camera would not be suitable for these uses.

Q4 Radio dials can be calibrated in terms of frequency or wavelength. Radio stations sometimes advertise the frequency of their broadcasts and sometimes the wavelength.

Radio station	Frequency/Hz	Wavelength/m
Atlantic 252	2.52×10^5	
Talk		285
radio 2	8.8×10^7	
radio Scotland		3.25
radio Manx	1.37×10^6	

The wave equation $v = f\lambda$ can be used to calculate the frequency if the wavelength is known, or calculate the wavelength if the frequency is known.

Use the wave equation, taking the speed of radio waves as 3×10^8 m/s, to work out the quantities not shown in the table.

Q5 Radio 4 is broadcast on long wave at a wavelength of 1500 m and on VHF at a wavelength of 3 m.

    a) Explain why only one transmitter is needed for the long-wave broadcast to cover the whole of the country but a network of transmitters is needed for the VHF broadcast.

    b) The radio 4 VHF broadcast is in stereo but the long-wave broadcast is in mono. Explain why stereo is not used for the long-wave broadcast.

Q6 Copper cable telephone links are rapidly being replaced by optical fibres, both for long distance and local communication.
Describe the advantages of using optical fibres for telephone calls.

Q7 The diagram shows how microwaves are focused into a narrow beam before being transmitted to a repeater station which then amplifies them before sending them on to other repeater stations.

   a) Explain why the microwaves need to be transmitted in a narrow beam.

   b) Explain why microwaves are used for this purpose rather than longer wavelength radio waves.

A satellite used for communications acts like a repeater station, except that the waves have to be transmitted over a much greater distance. The dishes are limited in size to a few metres in diameter, depending on which rocket is used for the launch.

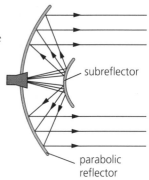

subreflector

parabolic reflector

   c) Explain why the microwaves used in satellite transmissions have a very short wavelength of a few millimetres.

   d) Why is a 'decoder' necessary to receive satellite television transmissions?

C6 – C7 Telecommunications

- Digital signals are preferred to analogue signals in telecommunications – noise and distortion can be removed easily from a digital signal.
- In radio transmissions, the radio wave carries the sound using amplitude modulation (AM) or frequency modulation (FM) – higher quality reception is possible with FM.
- According to their frequency, radio waves travel as ground waves (low frequency), sky waves (medium frequency) or space waves (high frequency).

Q1 A telephone handset contains two transducers. Identify the two transducers in a telephone handset and describe the function of each one.

Q2 Which option describes the difference between an analogue signal and a digital signal?

   A An analogue signal can vary continuously but a digital signal can only have certain values.

   B A digital signal can vary continuously but an analogue signal can only have certain values.

C An analogue signal is used to transmit speech; a digital is used
for pictures.

D A digital signal is used to transmit speech; an analogue is used
for pictures.

Q3 **a)** Explain why sound cannot be transmitted directly as a radio wave.

b) Sketch displacement–time graphs that show:

i) a radio wave carrying a sound wave using amplitude modulation

ii) a radio wave carrying a sound wave using frequency modulation.

Q4 **a)** Use diagrams to show the different methods of propagation of ground
waves, sky waves and space waves.

b) Which type of wave is used for:

i) satellite transmissions?

ii) amateur radio enthusiasts who wish to communicate with
enthusiasts in other countries?

Q5 Radio waves that use FM use a range of frequencies, called a bandwidth,
rather than just one frequency. Speech needs a bandwidth of 3.4 kHz.
Music needs a bandwidth of 20 kHz.

a) What range of frequencies would be required if radio 4 long wave
(frequency = 200 kHz) transmitted music using frequency modulation?

b) What range of frequencies is required for radio 4 VHF
(frequency = 90 MHz) to transmit music?

c) Give one **advantage** and one **disadvantage** of a music station
broadcasting on VHF rather than on long wave.

37 X-rays and gamma rays

■ X-rays and gamma rays are short-wavelength, high energy
electromagnetic radiation – they are very penetrative forms of
ionising radiation.

■ X-rays are used to take photographs. They pass through body tissue
but are absorbed by bone.

■ Gamma rays are used as medical tracers to show blood flow or to
concentrate in one particular organ.

Q1 Which option describes the **main** difference between X-rays and
gamma rays?

A X-rays have a shorter wavelength than gamma rays.

B X-rays have a longer wavelength than gamma rays.

C X-rays come from unstable nuclei but gamma rays are generated in
gamma-ray tubes.

D Gamma rays come from unstable nuclei but X-rays are generated in
X-ray tubes.

Q2 Explain how the properties of X-rays make them suitable for examining broken bones.

Q3 X-rays and gamma rays are both forms of **ionising** radiation.
   a) What happens when an atom is ionised?
   b) Ionisation of water in cells can lead to the formation of hydrogen peroxide. Explain why this is undesirable.
   c) Why is it particularly important that sex cells are protected from X-rays and gamma rays?
   d) Suggest how the sex cells of a patient receiving X-ray or gamma-ray treatment can be protected.

Q4 When X-rays are used to treat cancers, the patient is exposed to X-ray beams from several different directions. These overlap at the area being treated. Why are several overlapping beams used instead of just one beam?

Q5 Iodine-131 decays by emitting both beta and gamma radiation. When absorbed by the body, it concentrates in the thyroid gland. It has a half-life of 8 days.
   Iodine-131 was released into the atmosphere after the Chernobyl accident.
   a) Explain why people living around Chernobyl were given iodine tablets to counteract the harmful effects of iodine-131.
   Iodine-131 can be used to investigate the activity of the thyroid gland. More recently it has been replaced with iodine-123. Iodine-123 has a half-life of thirteen hours and emits gamma radiation only.
   b) Suggest how iodine-131 can be used to compare the activity of a 'suspect' thyroid gland with that of a 'normal' one.
   c) Explain why iodine-123 is now preferred to iodine-131.

38 Earth waves

■ Earth tremors cause waves to travel to parts of the Earth's surface.
■ Longitudinal waves, or P waves, can travel through solids and liquids and they are detected all over the Earth's surface.
■ S waves are transverse and cannot travel through liquids. The fact that S waves do not travel through the centre of the Earth gives evidence that the Earth's outer core is liquid.
■ L waves are long wavelength waves that travel through the Earth's crust.

Q1 The Earth is thought to have a solid iron core surrounded by a liquid outer core. The core is solid because:
   A it is cooler than the outer core   B it is warmer than the outer core
   C it is at a low pressure   D it is at a high pressure.

Q2 The mantle, the part of the Earth just below the crust, is thought to be hot and fluid. What evidence is there for the mantle being hot and fluid?

Q3 The diagram shows the centre of an earthquake.

epicentre

    a) Label on the diagram the regions where P waves could be detected.

    b) Label on the diagram where S waves would be detected.

    c) Explain why P waves can be detected over a larger area of the Earth's surface than S waves can.

Q4 Twenty minutes after an earthquake, a seismometer on the Earth's surface directly opposite the epicentre detects the arrival of waves. A second set of waves follows forty minutes later.

    a) Identify each type of wave.

    b) Give **two** reasons why the second set of waves took three times as long as the first set to reach the seismometer.

    c) Sketch a possible seismographic record showing the two sets of waves. At another point on the Earth's surface closer to the epicentre, a seismometer detects the first set of waves after only five minutes, with two further sets following.

    d) Explain why this seismometer detects three sets of waves.

    e) Sketch a seismographic record showing the three sets of waves.

    f) P waves travel through the body of the Earth at an average speed of 10 km/s. Use this value to calculate the distance between the closer seismometer and the epicentre.

Q5 Explain how seismographic records provide evidence that the Earth has a layered structure.

D The Earth and its place in the Universe

39–40 Gravitational forces

- There are nine known planets in orbit around our Sun. The four inner planets are dense and rocky.
- Asteroids are rocky fragments that orbit the Sun inbetween the inner and outer planets.
- The five outer planets are cooler than the inner ones. They are thought to be made up largely of gases and ice.
- Gravitational forces are attractive forces that exist between massive objects.
- The Sun's gravitational pull on the planets, asteroids and comets keeps them in orbit. Moons are kept in orbit by the gravitational pull of their planet.
- The strength of a body's gravitational field decreases with increasing distance from the body.

Q1 The table gives some information about the inner planets.

Planet	Mass/kg	Radius/km	Density /g per cm³	Time to rotate on its own axis /Earth days	Time to orbit the Sun /Earth years	Average distance from Sun compared with Earth
Earth	6.0×10^{24}	6380	5.5	1	1.00	1.0
Mars	6.4×10^{23}	3400	3.9	1	1.90	1.5
Mercury	3.3×10^{23}	2440	5.4	59	0.24	0.4
Venus	4.9×10^{24}	6050	5.3	240	0.60	0.7

a) Write a list of the inner planets in order of their distance from the Sun.

b) Give **two** reasons why the time to orbit the Sun increases with increasing distance from the Sun.

Venus has been described as 'the Earth's twin sister'.

c) In what ways is Venus similar to the Earth?

The inner planets are sometimes called the dense planets.

d) Use the data in the table to explain how the density is related to distance from the Sun.

An astronomer observes Mercury from the Earth and repeats the observation one year later.

e) How many orbits of the Sun has Mercury completed between the observations?

f) How many rotations on its axis has Mercury completed between the observations?

g) Suggest why early astronomers thought that Mercury's orbit time is the same as the time it takes to rotate on its axis.

Venus' rotation about its axis is in the opposite direction to that of the other inner planets.

h) What else is unusual about the rotation of Venus about its axis?

Q2 The asteroid belt lies between the inner and the outer planets.
  a) Which two planets are closest to the asteroid belt?
  b) Which of these planets is likely to have the greater effect on the orbits of asteroids?

Approximately ten meteorites, or rocks from space, are known to reach the Earth's surface each year. Most of these come from the asteroid belt.

  c) Suggest how asteroids become meteorites.
  d) Explain why it is likely that many more than ten meteorites hit the Earth's surface each year.

Most of the rocks from space that approach the Earth do not reach the surface.

  e) Suggest what happens to them.

Q3 There are many asteroids outside the asteroid belt. More than a thousand are known to cross the Earth's orbit each year. The diagram shows the orbit of such an asteroid, called an interloper. Pieces of rock from Mars have been found on the Earth's surface. Suggest how an interloper could have caused this.

Q4 The data in the table concern the orbits of the four inner planets and Jupiter.
  a) Describe the link between orbital speed and distance from the Sun.
  b) Draw a graph of orbital speed (*y*-axis) against distance (*x*-axis) from the Sun.

Ceres, the largest asteroid, has a mean distance from the Sun that is 2.77 times that of the Earth.

  c) Use your graph to find the mean orbital speed of Ceres.

Planet	Mean distance from Sun (Earth = 1)	Mean orbital speed /km per s
Mercury	0.39	47.9
Venus	0.72	35.0
Earth	1.00	29.8
Mars	1.52	24.1
Jupiter	5.20	13.1

Q5 The surface temperature of a planet depends on its distance from the Sun and its atmosphere. All atmospheres have a 'greenhouse effect' that reduces the amount of energy radiating into space.

Mercury has no atmosphere. Venus has a very dense atmosphere of carbon dioxide and sulphur dioxide.

a) Explain why the surface of Mercury is cratered like the Earth's moon.
At any time, the temperature at the surface of Mercury ranges between
−200°C and 400°C.
b) Explain why there is such a big temperature range.
Venus and Earth have much smaller temperature ranges. At the surface
of Venus, the temperature is a fairly constant 450° C.
c) Explain why there is a small temperature range on the surfaces of
Venus and Earth.
d) Suggest two reasons why Venus is considerably hotter than Earth.
Space probes sent to examine the surface of Venus have had very
short lives.
e) Suggest reasons for this.

Q6 Comets orbit the Sun at distances up to 50 000 times that between the
Earth and the Sun. Their orbital times range from a few years to over a
million years.
   a) Describe **two** differences between the orbit of a comet and that
   of a planet.
   b) Explain how the structure of a comet changes as it passes close to
   the Sun.
   c) Explain how the orbital paths of some comets can be changed as
   they pass within the planetary system.

D1 Satellites

■ For an object to travel in a circle, there needs to be an unbalanced
force directed towards the centre. The size of the unbalanced force is
given by the formula: $F = mv^2/r$
■ The unbalanced force acting on a satellite is the gravitational force
between the satellite and the planet.
■ The orbit time of a satellite increases with increasing distance from
the planet.

Q1 Which diagram shows the forces acting on a satellite in orbit around
the Earth?

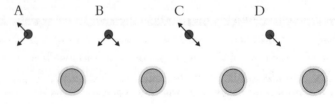

Q2 Which statement is true?

A An object following a circular path is changing speed all the time.

B An object following a circular path is changing direction all the time.

C An object following a circular path experiences a force pushing it outwards.

D The forces acting on an object following a circular path are balanced.

Q3 The table shows how the orbit time of a satellite depends on the height of the satellite above the surface of the Earth.

Height above surface of the Earth /10^6 m	Orbit time /hours
10	5.8
20	11.8
30	19.1
40	27.5
50	36.9

a) Draw a graph of height above the surface of the Earth (y-axis) against orbit time (x-axis).

b) Describe what your graph shows about the way in which the orbit time of a satellite changes with increasing height.

c) Deduce from your graph the height above the Earth's surface of a satellite that orbits the Earth in 24 hours.

d) Suggest a use of a satellite that has an orbit time of 24 hours.

Some weather satellites occupy very low orbits.

e) Use your graph to estimate the orbit time of a low-orbit satellite.

Q4 a) Use your answer to **Q3 c)** to calculate the speed of a satellite in a geostationary orbit. The radius of the Earth is 6.4×10^6 m.

b) Calculate the size of the unbalanced force on a geostationary satellite that has a mass of 250 kg.

c) Explain why a geostationary satellite does not need any engines to maintain its orbit.

Q5 Kepler was an astronomer who put forward three laws that summarised the behaviour of planets. One of his laws is that r^3/T^2 has the same value for all planets, where r is the distance of the planet from the Sun and T is the orbital time.

a) Use the data given in **Q3** and **Q4** to decide if the same law applies to satellites of the Earth.

b) Use the law to predict the orbit time of the Moon. The distance between the Earth and the Moon is 3.84×10^8 m.

41–2 Stars and galaxies

- Stars form in clouds of dust and gas, drawn together by gravitational forces.
- After a star's main sequence, it expands and cools, becoming a red giant. A small star then contracts to become a white dwarf.
- Large stars can become blue supergiants, forming the more massive elements by the fusion of helium nuclei. Once these reactions cease, the star expands, then contracts and glows very brightly as a supernova before exploding. ·
- New stars can be formed from the remnants of an exploded supernova.
- The Universe is known to be expanding. The rate of expansion is estimated by measuring the 'red shift' of light from stars.
- Time may have started with an enormous explosion, called the 'big bang'.
- The future of the Universe depends on whether the gravitational forces are strong enough to stop the expansion.

Q1 Choose the option that gives the main reaction in a star in its main sequence:
A helium nuclei fuse to form hydrogen nuclei
B helium nuclei fuse to form larger nuclei
C hydrogen nuclei fuse to form helium nuclei
D helium nuclei fission to form hydrogen nuclei.

Q2 The way in which we are able to see a star is not the same as the way in which we are able to see planets.
Describe how seeing stars is different from seeing planets.

Q3 New stars are formed in giant clouds of dust and hydrogen gas.
The temperature inside these clouds is around 15 K.
a) Describe the formation of a new star in a dust cloud.
b) Explain how heavy elements in the Earth could have formed at the centre of a large star.
c) Describe the sequence of events that could have led to the formation of our Sun.
Our Sun is a small star in its main sequence.
d) What is likely to happen to our Sun in the future?

Q4 The graph on the next page shows the results of measuring the speeds of galaxies moving away from the Milky Way.
a) Describe what this graph shows.
Hubble put forward the theory that the speed of a galaxy relative to the Milky Way is proportional to its distance from the Milky Way.

b) Explain whether the graph supports Hubble's theory.
c) Use a diagram to explain how the Universe could have originated at one point.

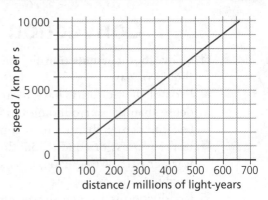

Q5 a) What is the meaning of the term 'red shift'?
b) How does the light received from a star approaching the Earth differ from that received from a star going away from the Earth?

Q6 Space has a temperature. It is filled with microwave energy at a temperature of about 3 K.
a) Explain how this provides evidence in favour of the 'big bang' theory.
b) What is likely to happen to the temperature of space as the Universe continues to expand?

Q7 When nuclei of light elements such as helium, carbon and oxygen are formed by fusion, energy is released. The formation of iron and heavier elements by fusion requires energy.
a) Why does a star cool when it is forming iron and heavier elements?
b) What is likely to happen to a star after it starts to form the heavy elements? Describe a possible sequence of events.

E Energy

43–4 Convection and conduction

■ Convection currents transfer energy by movement of parts of a fluid (liquid or gas).

■ Parts of the fluid that have been warmed expand and become less dense than the surrounding fluid. Parts that have been cooled become denser than their surroundings and so sink.

■ In the process of conduction, the more energetic molecules in the warmer part of the material pass on some of their energy to neighbouring molecules.

■ Conduction is a much slower process in gases than it is in solids and liquids because the molecules are spread more widely.

■ Metals are much better conductors than non-metals. Metals have free electrons that can move rapidly and transfer the energy to all parts of the metal.

Q1 Which statement is true?
  A Convection currents are caused by heat rising.
  B Convection currents are caused by cold sinking.
  C Convection only takes place in gases.
  D Convection currents cannot occur in solids.

Q2 An ice cube floats in a glass of water.
Describe and explain the movement of the water around the ice cube.

Q3 Convection currents can be very effective in removing heat from the body.
  a) Explain why it is comfortable to wear tight-fitting clothes in cold weather.
  b) Explain why it is comfortable to wear loose-fitting clothes in warm weather.

Q4 Central-heating radiators heat a room mainly by convection currents. The diagram shows the position of a central-heating radiator in a room.
  a) Draw arrows to show the movement of air in the room when the radiator is hot.
  b) Whereabouts is the warmest air in the room?

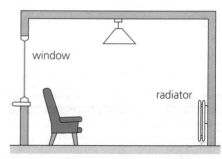

  c) Whereabouts in the room would you expect to find a downwards-driven convection current on a cold day? Draw and label an arrow on your diagram to show this.

d) Explain why an older person who spends much of the day sitting down could feel uncomfortable if this is the only source of heat in the room.

In wet weather, some people dry clothes indoors by spreading them over a central-heating radiator.

e) Explain how this reduces the effectiveness of the central heating.

Q5 Explain each of the following.
  a) Copper is a better conductor of thermal energy than iron is.
  b) Metals are good conductors of electricity as well as being good thermal conductors.
  c) You lose body heat more quickly when your clothing is wet than when it is dry.
  d) Metal objects at room temperature often feel colder than non-metal objects at the same temperature.

Q6 For each of the following, state whether it is better to use a good or a poor conductor. Give a reason for your answer in each case and state what other factors affect the choice of material.
  a) the glass door in an oven
  b) a hot water tank
  c) a hot water radiator
  d) a spoon used for stirring the contents of a saucepan.

Q7 The graph shows how the volume of a sample of water changes between the temperatures 0°C and 8°C.

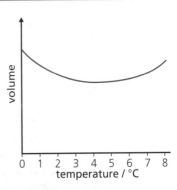

  a) At what temperature is the density of water greatest? Explain how you can tell.

On a cold night, a garden pond cools from the surface.

  b) Describe the movement of water in the pond as it cools from a temperature of 8°C.
  c) Explain why convection currents in the pond stop before the water freezes.
  d) Explain why fish in the pond are unlikely to be harmed when it freezes over.

Q8 In an experiment to test thermal conduction, some strips of heat-sensitive paper are placed at 5 cm intervals along a copper bar.

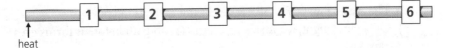

heat

The bar is placed horizontally and heated at one end. As each strip of paper changes colour, the time taken is recorded. The table shows the results.

Strip number	1	2	3	4	5	6
Time taken for strip to change colour/s	12	27	45	65	87	111

a) What does this data show about the rate of energy flow at different parts of the bar? Explain how you can tell.

b) Suggest why the rate of energy flow changes in this way.

c) Apart from the distance from the heat source, write down **two** other factors that affect the time it takes for the first strip to change colour.

It is suggested that the test should be carried out with the bar vertical, using a beaker of hot oil as the heat source.

d) Explain why this would not be satisfactory.

45 Radiant energy

- Everything emits and absorbs infrared radiation.
- The hotter the object, the more energy it emits each second.
- Dark, dull surfaces are better than light, shiny surfaces at giving out and absorbing infrared radiation.
- Foil can be effective at keeping things hot or cold because it reflects infrared radiation in the same way that it reflects light.

Q1 Whereabouts does infrared radiation fit in the electromagnetic spectrum?
A between X-rays and gamma rays
B between light and ultraviolet radiation
C between radio waves and microwaves
D between light and microwaves.

Q2 Here is a list of clothes that can be worn on a sunny day:
black trousers   red teeshirt   white shirt
black shorts   yellow blouse
a) Which two items are the best emitters of infrared radiation?
b) Which two items are the best absorbers of infrared radiation?

Q3 Explain the reasons for the following.
a) Household radiators are usually painted white.
b) Frozen food bought from a supermarket can be kept cool by keeping it in a foil-lined container.
c) Commercial aircraft are often painted white or silver.
d) The water pipes of a solar water heater are painted black.
e) On a clear night, ice forms on a tarmac footpath before it forms on a grass lawn.

Q4 In spring, farmers sometimes cover ground where seed has been planted with clear polythene sheet.
Explain how this can speed up the germination of the seed.

Q5 Overheating of the transistors in an amplifier could cause permanent damage. To prevent this, some transistors are mounted on a heat sink. The job of the heat sink is to keep the transistor cool.
The heat sink is made of metal, usually aluminium, that has a dull, black finish.
Explain how the processes of conduction, convection and radiation are involved in keeping the transistor cool.

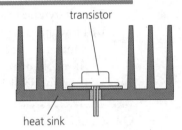

46 Evaporation

- Evaporation happens when energetic molecules leave a liquid and form a vapour.
- As a liquid evaporates it cools and takes in energy from its surroundings. This is an important process in the control of body temperature.
- Thermal insulation is designed to reduce energy losses by convection, conduction, radiation and evaporation.
- Effective insulation involves using a combination of lids and covers, foil and trapped air.

Q1 Which is the best description of evaporation?
    A Molecules from the body of the liquid rise to the surface.
    B Energetic molecules leave the surface of a liquid.
    C Bubbles of vapour form in a liquid.
    D Bubbles of air rise to the surface of a liquid.

Q2 The diagram represents a molecule in the surface of a liquid.
    a) Draw arrows to represent the forces acting on the molecule.
    b) Explain why the resultant force is down.
    c) Suggest why the attractive forces from air particles are negligible.
    d) State **two** conditions necessary for the molecule to leave the surface of the liquid.
    e) Explain how the speed of the molecule changes as it leaves the surface.

Q3 Expanded polystyrene is often used as an insulator.
A child's drink container uses expanded polystyrene
between the inner and outer walls.
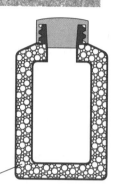
   a) Explain why the structure of expanded
      polystyrene makes it an effective insulator.
   b) How important is it to keep the lid on the
      container if it holds:
      i) a cold drink
      ii) a hot drink?

expanded
polystyrene beads

Q4 Cool bags are useful for keeping bottles and
cans of drinks cool in hot weather. Air is
trapped in several layers between the inner and
outer walls.
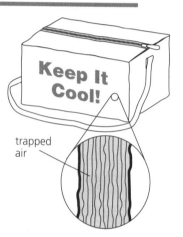
   a) Explain how the trapped air reduces energy
      transfer into the cool bag.
   b) Why are several layers of air more effective
      than a single air gap?
   c) Some manufacturers of cool bags use a sheet
      of metal foil as a lining for the outer wall.
      Describe the purpose of this.
   d) Discuss whether the colour of the cool bag
      affects its ability to keep the contents cool.

trapped
air

47 Insulating a house

- Energy is lost from warm houses in a variety of ways.
- Draughts can remove warm air through badly-fitting doors
  and windows.
- Energy is transferred by conduction and convection through walls,
  the roof, windows and floors.
- All parts of a house radiate energy.
- Common methods of insulating a house include double glazing and
  loft and cavity wall insulation.

Q1 A central heating system is used to keep the interior of a house at a
constant 21°C when the outside temperature is 10°C.
Which of the following statements is correct?
   A No energy flows out of the house.
   B Energy flows into the house at the same rate as it flows out.
   C The rate of energy flow into the house is greater than the rate of
     energy flow out of the house.
   D The rate of energy flow into the house is less than the rate of energy
     flow out of the house.

Q2 A householder wishes to improve her house by eliminating all draughts.
   a) What are the causes of draughts in a house?
   b) What is the danger in eliminating draughts and what advice would you give the householder to avoid this?

Q3 The diagram represents an uninsulated cavity wall.
   a) Explain how energy flows through the wall by conduction and convection when the interior is warmer than the exterior.
   b) Explain how filling the cavity with foam or mineral wool reduces the energy flow.
   Many houses in this country are constructed from unpainted brick.
   c) How is cavity wall insulation likely to affect the temperature inside the house in sunny weather?

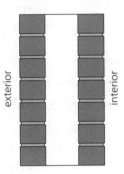

Q4 a) Few householders attempt to reduce the energy radiated from a house. By considering the different parts of the structure of a house, explain why: i) only a small proportion of the energy flow from a warm house is radiated ii) it would be impractical to try to stop this radiation from taking place.
   b) Explain why the energy flow from a warm house is greater in wet weather than in dry weather at the same temperature.

Q5 The conductivity of a building material is described by its U-value. The higher the U-value, the better the conductor. The U-value is the energy flow each second through $1 \, m^2$ of material for each °C difference in temperature. The table shows some U-values of insulated and uninsulated parts of a house.

Material	U-value/ $Wm^{-2}°C^{-1}$
uninsulated cavity wall	1.40
foam-insulated cavity wall	0.70
single-glazed window	5.50
double-glazed window	2.80
uninsulated roofspace	2.20
fibreglass-insulated roofspace	0.50

Typical costs of installing insulation in an average house are:
   double glazing   £5000
   cavity wall insulation £500
   loft insulation   £100
   a) Explain why loft insulation is more cost-effective than cavity wall insulation.
   b) Compare the effectiveness of double glazing and cavity wall insulation at reducing energy losses.
   Despite the high cost, double glazing is a popular home improvement.
   c) Suggest reasons for this.
   A room has an outside wall with an area of $6m^2$. It is an uninsulated cavity wall.

d) How much energy flows through the wall each second when the temperature of the inner surface is 15°C and the temperature of the outer surface is 5°C?

e) Compare your answer to **d)** with the energy flow through a similar size wall that has been insulated.

f) How is the energy flow through the insulated wall changed if the householder replaces some brickwork with a 2 m² double-glazed window?

48 Using energy resources

■ Our limited fuel reserves will last longer if they are used more efficiently.

■ The **efficiency** of an energy transfer is the percentage of the available energy that is transferred to a useful output.

■ Most power stations operate at an efficiency of less than 50%, with more than half of the available energy being wasted as heat in the surroundings.

■ Many of our current methods of using renewable energy sources are expensive to manufacture and have a low efficiency, so limiting their use.

Q1 Which of the following are renewable energy resources?
A coal   B wood   C wind   D oil

Q2 An 'energy-efficient' lamp takes in energy from electricity at the rate of 20 J/s. It gives out energy as light at the rate of 5 J/s.
a) Suggest what happens to the energy that is not given out as light.
b) Calculate the efficiency of the lamp.
c) To what extent is 'energy-efficient' a fair description of such a lamp?

Q3 Wind turbines are becoming increasingly popular for generating electricity. A single turbine placed on top of a windy hill can provide all the electricity required by a farm.
Groups of turbines built in exposed areas such as the Yorkshire Moors can supply electricity into the national grid.
a) Describe the benefits of using wind turbines.
b) What are the drawbacks of wind turbines?
Some environmentalists are in favour of using wind turbines and others are against.
c) Suppose that there is a proposal to build a wind farm close to where you live.
Design a one-page leaflet putting the case either in favour of the proposal **or** against it.

Q4 The chart shows what proportion of electricity is generated from the main fuels used in power stations in the UK. Most of the hydroelectric power is generated in Scotland and Wales.

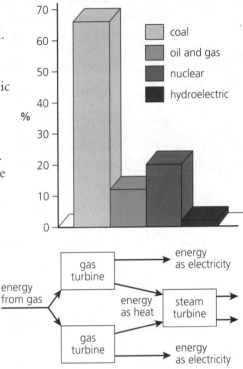

a) Explain why very little hydroelectric power is generated in England.

b) Suggest why the proportion of electricity generated from nuclear fuel could drop in the next decade.

As large, coal-burning power stations are coming to the end of their useful lives, they are being replaced by smaller, gas-burning stations. A typical gas-burning power station has three generators; two are driven by gas turbines that use the waste gases from burning the gas and the third is based on a steam turbine using the exhaust gases from the gas turbines.

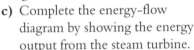

c) Complete the energy-flow diagram by showing the energy output from the steam turbine.

d) Suggest why gas turbines are used instead of using the gas to generate steam to drive a steam turbine.

e) This type of gas-burning power station is more efficient than a coal-burning one. Explain why less energy is wasted by a gas-burning power station.

49–50 Work, energy and power

■ When a force causes movement, it does work and transfers energy.

■ Work and energy transfer are measured in joules (J) and are calculated using the formula:

work done or energy transfer = force × distance moved in its own direction

or $W = F \times d$

■ The **power** of a device describes the amount of work done or energy transferred each second. Power is measured in watts (W) and is calculated using the formula:

power = energy transferred or work done ÷ time taken or $P = E/t$

Q1 Which of the following forces are working?
A The Earth's pull on a falling apple.
B The Earth's pull on a car parked on a hill.
C The electric force that causes a current in a lamp filament.
D The push of a bookshelf on some books.

Q2 Calculate the amount of work done when:
a) a 65 N force pushes a cyclist for 80 m
b) a 1400 N force accelerates a car over a distance of 250 m
c) a 2200 N force is used to move a lift and its passengers through a vertical height of 7.5 m.

Q3 A clock in a church tower is driven by a piece of stone that is allowed to fall slowly down the tower. As the stone nears the bottom of the tower, it has to be lifted up again.
The stone weighs 1200 N and the height of the lift is 7.8 m.
a) Calculate the energy transferred to the stone when it is lifted up.

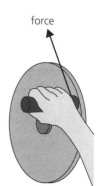

force

As the stone is too heavy to lift directly, the person who winds the clock does so by turning a wheel that is connected to the stone through gears. A 250 N force is required to turn the wheel, which has a circumference of 1.2 m.
b) How much work is done when the clock winder turns the wheel through one revolution?
c) What is the minimum number of revolutions required to raise the stone?
The clock winder finds that the wheel has to be turned through precisely 33 revolutions to raise the stone.
d) Explain why more turns are required than you calculated in **c)**.
e) Calculate the efficiency of the clock winding mechanism.

Q4 Use the power equation in one of the three forms $E=P/t$, $P=Et$, $t=E/P$ to complete the table.

Power/W	Energy transfer/J	Time/s
	300	5
	150	60
60		300
1440		12
2.5	500	
2500		300

Q5 Calculate the power of:
a) a heater that transfers 2160 J of energy from electricity to heat in 60 s
b) an LED that transfers 18 J of energy from electricity to heat and light in 1 hour (3600 s)
c) a crane that lifts a 25 000 N load of bricks through a height of 14 m in 70 s.

Q6 A car is towing a caravan at a speed of 25 m/s. The pulling force is 1200 N.
    a) How much work is done each second in pulling the caravan?
    b) How much engine power is being used to tow the caravan?

Q7 A barrel which weighs 500 N is rolled up a ramp onto the back of a van.
The force used is 280 N and the distance up the ramp is 2.5 m. A second
barrel of the same weight is lifted onto the back of the van, which is
1.2 m from the ground.
    a) Calculate the work done in
each case.
    b) Do the barrels gain the same
amount of energy, or does one
gain more than the other?
    c) What is the advantage of using the ramp?

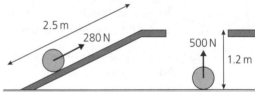

Q8 A car engine has a maximum power of 80 kW.
    a) How much work can it do in one second?
    b) It moves the car 45 m in one second. How big is the driving force?

51 K.e. and p.e.

◼ When an object is moved away from the Earth's surface it gains
gravitational potential energy, or potential energy (p.e.) for short.
◼ Falling objects lose potential energy as they lose height.
◼ The energy transfer due to such a change in position is calculated
using the formula:
    change in potential energy E_p = weight × change in height = $mg\Delta h$
◼ Moving objects have kinetic energy (k.e.). Kinetic energy depends on
the mass of the object and its (speed)^2.
◼ Kinetic energy is calculated using the formula:
$$\text{kinetic energy } E_k = \tfrac{1}{2} \times \text{mass} \times (\text{speed})^2 = \tfrac{1}{2}\, mv^2$$
◼ If an object is falling or rising freely with no other forces acting,
energy is transferred between kinetic and potential. The gain in
kinetic energy is exactly balanced by the loss in potential energy for
a falling object and vice versa for a rising object.

In the following questions, take g = 10 N/kg.

Q1 Which is the best description of the energy transfer when an object is
falling freely in the absence of resistive forces?
    A Kinetic energy is transferred to potential energy.
    B Potential energy is transferred to kinetic energy.
    C Movement energy is transferred to kinetic energy.
    D Kinetic energy is transferred to heat.

Q2 Calculate the kinetic energy of the following:
   a) a bus and its passengers with a total mass of 7600 kg travelling at 12 m/s
   b) a cycle and cyclist with a mass of 75 kg travelling at 6.5 m/s
   c) a golf ball of mass 0.05 kg travelling at 30 m/s.

Q3 Calculate the change in potential energy when:
   a) a hot-air balloon and passenger with a total mass of 280 kg rise through a vertical height of 150 m
   b) a 56 kg hurdler raises her centre of mass by 0.6 m to clear a hurdle
   c) a 2 kg mass in a grandfather clock falls through a distance of 1.5 m.

Q4 **a)** Calculate the kinetic energy of a 800 kg car travelling at 14 m/s.
   b) Calculate the kinetic energy of the same car travelling at 28 m/s.
   14 m/s is approximately 30 mph.
   c) What advice would you give to a driver who travels at 60 mph in a built-up area where the speed limit is 30 mph? Use a scientific argument to support your answer.

Q5 A child and his swing have a mass of 35 kg. The maximum speed of the child is 2.6 m/s.
   a) Calculate the maximum kinetic energy of the child and swing.
   b) When the child reaches his maximum height, what is the value of the:
      i) kinetic energy?
      ii) gravitational potential energy?
   c) Calculate the maximum vertical distance that the child moves through.

Q6 **a)** Calculate the kinetic energy of a 0.6 kg ball which is thrown upwards at 12.5 m/s.
   b) How much potential energy does it have at its maximum height?
   c) How high does it go?

F Molecular physics
F1 Moving particles

■ Brownian motion and diffusion provide evidence that the particles in liquids and gases are moving.
■ The particles in liquids and gases move at high speeds in unpredictable directions. Gas particles move much greater distances between collisions than liquid particles do.
■ The particles of a solid vibrate about fixed positions. Like those of liquids and gases, their energy depends on the temperature.

Q1 Which is the best description of the movement of the particles in a liquid?
A They move freely, occasionally colliding with other particles.
B They vibrate about fixed positions.
C They move slowly, occasionally colliding with other particles.
D They jostle, and constantly collide with other particles.

Q2 Brownian motion can be seen by examining the motion of smoke specks in air using a low-power microscope.
a) Describe the motion of the smoke specks.
Air particles cannot be seen even with the highest power optical microscope.
b) What does this tell you about the relative sizes of smoke specks and air particles?
c) Explain how the slow movement of the smoke specks indicates that air particles are moving much more rapidly.

Q3 Use the particle model to explain each of the following.
a) Diffusion in liquids is a much slower process than diffusion in gases.
b) Solids have a fixed shape but liquids can change their shape.
c) Gases have no shape at all.

Q4 The diagram shows a model of particles in a solid, made using polystyrene spheres.
a) Describe the movement of the spheres when they represent a solid.
The particles that make the model are given more energy so that they represent the particles in a liquid.
b) How does the spacing of the spheres change when the model changes from a model of a solid to a model of a liquid?
c) How does the movement of the spheres change when the model changes from a model of a solid to a model of a liquid?
d) Sketch the appearance of the model when it is used to show the particles in a gas.
e) How does this model explain gas pressure?

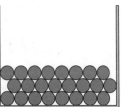

Q5 A small quantity of liquid bromine is
introduced into two sealed glass tubes.
One of the tubes was previously
evacuated, the other contained air at
atmospheric pressure. The diagram shows
the glass tubes five minutes after the
bromine is introduced.
The average speed of bromine molecules at
room temperature is 150 m/s.
The tubes are 30 cm tall.

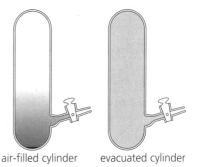

air-filled cylinder   evacuated cylinder

    a) Estimate the time it takes for the bromine vapour to fill the
evacuated tube.

    b) Explain why it takes much longer for the bromine to travel through
the air-filled tube.

52 Gases under pressure

- Gases exert pressure due to collisions between the particles of the
gas and the walls of the container.
- Compressing a gas increases the frequency of the collisions so the
pressure is increased.
- For a fixed mass of gas whose temperature does not change, the
pressure is inversely proportional to the volume. This is known as
Boyle's law and can be written as:

$$pV = \text{constant} \quad \text{or} \quad p \propto 1/V$$

Q1 The pressure of some gas in a sealed container is changed, the
temperature remaining the same. Which statement is correct?
A If the pressure is doubled, the volume also doubles.
B If the pressure is halved, the volume doubles.
C If the pressure is halved, the volume halves.
D If the pressure is doubled, the volume reduces to a quarter.

Q2 The diagram represents the particles in a sample of air.

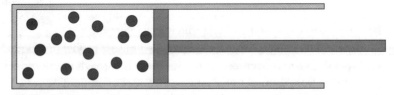

    a) Add arrows to show how the particles could be moving.
The piston is pulled out so that the gas occupies double its
original volume.

b) Draw a diagram to show the effect this has on the air particles.

c) What effect does this have on the pressure of the air?

Q3 The table shows the results of an experiment to find out how the pressure of a trapped gas changes when its volume is reduced.

Volume/cm³	50	43	35	24	17	14	10
Pressure/10⁵ Pa	1	1.2	1.4	2.1	2.9	3.6	5

a) Use these results to plot a graph of pressure against volume. Draw the best curve.

b) Read off from your graph the volume of the gas when the pressure is:
   i) 2.0×10^5 Pa
   ii) 4.0×10^5 Pa.

c) What do your answers to **b)** indicate about the effect of doubling the pressure on a gas?

d) Use the results to plot a graph of pressure against 1/volume.

e) Explain how your graph of pressure against 1/volume shows that the pressure is proportional to 1/volume.

Q4 A carbon dioxide gas cylinder contains 180 cm³ of gas at a pressure of 6.3×10^6 Pa.

a) Calculate the volume of the gas at atmospheric pressure, 1.0×10^5 Pa. The cylinder valve is opened and the gas is collected at atmospheric pressure.

b) Explain why less gas is collected than the answer to **a)**.
Carbon dioxide does not liquify when put under pressure. Butane, used for camping gas, does liquify.

c) Explain how the cylinders used to store carbon dioxide are different from those used to store camping gas.

F2 Pressure and temperature

■ The pressure of a gas whose volume does not change is directly proportional to its temperature measured on the kelvin scale. This can be written as: $p/T =$ constant   or $p \propto T$

■ The formula for converting Celsius temperatures into kelvin temperatures is: T in $K = T$ in $°C + 273$

■ The gas equation can be used when the pressure, volume and temperature of a gas change.
It can be written as: $pV/T =$ constant   or $pV \propto T$

Q1 Potassium melts at 64°C and boils at 760°C.
   a) Write down the melting and boiling points of potassium in kelvin.
Oxygen melts at 54 K and boils at 90 K.
   b) Write down the melting and boiling points of oxygen in °C.

Q2 A carbon dioxide cylinder contains gas at a pressure of 7.5×10^6 Pa at a temperature of 20°C. The cylinder is immersed in boiling water at a temperature of 100°C.
Calculate the pressure of the gas at 100°C.

Q3 The pressure of a gas in a sealed container is measured over a range of temperatures. The table shows these measurements.

Pressure/10⁵ Pa	0.98	1.06	1.16	1.19	1.24	1.29
Temperature/°C	12	34	55	72	86	100

   a) Use the data to plot a graph of pressure (*y*-axis) against temperature (*x*-axis). Use a range of –300°C to +100°C for the scale on the *x*-axis, and a pressure scale starting at zero.
   b) By extrapolating your graph to zero pressure, make an estimate of the absolute zero of temperature on the Celsius scale.
   c) Suggest one way in which a more precise estimate of the absolute zero of temperature can be made.
   d) What property of the gas used for the measurements limits the range of the data available?

Q4 Gas pressure is due to collisions between the particles of the gas and the walls of the container.
   a) Write down **two** reasons why the pressure of a gas increases when the temperature rises.
   b) Explain how the pressure due to a gas differs from that due to a solid resting on a horizontal surface.

Q5 In a diesel engine, 400 cm³ of air at a temperature of 10°C and a pressure of 1.0×10^5 Pa is squashed into a volume of 35 cm³. The temperature rises to 500°C. Calculate the pressure of the squashed air.

F3 Heat specifics

■ The energy transfer when an object changes temperature can be calculated using the formula:

energy transfer = mass × specific heat capacity × temperature change

or $E = mc\Delta T$

■ Energy is absorbed when a solid melts and when a liquid vaporises. Energy is released when a liquid solidifies and when a gas or vapour condenses. The energy absorbed or released is called latent heat. It can be calculated using the formula:

energy transfer = mass × specific latent heat   or $E = mL$

Q1 The table shows the specific heat capacities of some materials. Calculate the energy transfer when:
  a) 4 kg of water is heated from 10°C to 15°C
  b) 10 kg of aluminium cools from 250°C to 20°C
  c) 3 kg of sand is heated from 10°C to 25°C
  d) 20 kg of air cools from 22°C to −4°C
  e) A 0.5 kg copper kettle containing 1.5 kg of water is heated from 15°C to 100°C.

Material	Specific heat capacity / J per kg°C
air	1100
aluminium	880
copper	380
sand	800
water	4200

Q2 A deep-fat frier contains 1.4 kg of oil at 20°C. The specific heat capacity of the oil is 2150 J/kg°C.
  a) Calculate the energy required to heat the oil to a temperature of 280°C.
  b) The frier has a 2 kW heater. How long does it take the heater to heat the oil from 20°C to 280°C?
  c) Write down **two** reasons why it takes longer than the answer to **b)** for the oil to heat up.

Q3 Good cooks recommend that before cooking potatoes in hot oil, the potatoes should first be dried. This causes less cooling of the oil when the potatoes are placed in it.
  Explain why drying the potatoes causes less cooling of the oil.

Q4 A chiropodist keeps a supply of liquid nitrogen in a flask. The specific latent heat of vaporisation for nitrogen is 2.5×10^5 J/kg. Heat from the warm room passes through the walls of the flask at the rate of 2.5 J/s. How long does it take for 1 kg of liquid nitrogen to turn into vapour?

Q5 The specific latent heat of vaporisation of water is 2.26×10^6 J/kg and that of ethanol is 0.85×10^6 J/kg.
  a) Suggest why some spilt water takes longer to dry than the same quantity of spilt ethanol.
  b) Explain why a drop of ethanol placed on the hand causes it to feel cool.

Q6 An electric shower has a heating element with a power of 8.4 kW. Water enters the boiler at a temperature of 11°C and leaves at a temperature of 45°C. Use the specific heat capacity of water in **Q1** to calculate the mass of water flowing through the shower each second.

F4 **Changing size**

■ For the same temperature rise, gases expand more than liquids which expand more than solids.
■ Bimetallic strips used in thermostats rely on the different expansion rates of two different metals.
■ The change in length when an object expands or contracts can be calculated using the formula:
change in length = initial length × linear expansivity × temperature change
$$\text{or} \quad e = l\,\alpha\,\Delta T$$

Q1 In a central heating system, the copper pipes that carry the hot water pass through holes in the wooden beams between the upstairs and downstairs of a house. Explain how this can cause creaking after the system has been turned on and after it has been turned off.

Q2 The diagram represents part of a large concrete bridge.
a) Explain the purpose of the gaps.
Normally these gaps are filled with a spongy material.
b) Explain why the gaps are filled and why a spongy material is used.
c) Why do the ends of the beam rest on rollers?

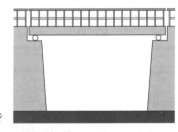

Q3 The table gives the expansivity of some common materials at room temperature.

Material	Expansivity/per K
iron	1.2×10^{-5}
glass	8.0×10^{-6}
aluminium	2.5×10^{-5}
brass	1.9×10^{-5}
concrete	1.2×10^{-5}

A 12 m span of a concrete bridge has to withstand a temperature variation of −10°C (cold winter night) to +30°C (hot summer day).
a) Calculate the difference in the length of the bridge at these temperature extremes.

Brass and iron are commonly used together in bimetallic strips.
A strip of brass and a strip of iron are joined together at room temperature.
b) Sketch the appearance of the strip after is has been placed:
  i) in a freezer   ii) in an oven.
c) Estimate the difference in length of each side of a 2 m × 1.5 m glass
  window between its extremes of temperature. Explain whether it is
  necessary to allow for this change in length when glazing domestic
  window frames.

Q4 An aluminium overhead cable is supported every 120 m.
The cable is positioned in summer at a temperature of 20°C.
Allowance is made for a lowest temperature of –20°C. How much
additional cable should be allowed between each pair of supports?

F5 Fluids

■ The more viscous a fluid, the more it resists the flow of objects
through it.
■ The rate at which a fluid flows through a tube depends on the
pressure gradient as well as the viscosity of the fluid.

Q1 Which of the following fluids is the most viscous at room temperature?
A cooking oil   B paraffin   C glucose syrup   D water

Q2 In an experiment to compare the viscosity of oil at different temperatures,
the time taken for a measured volume of oil to flow from a burette tap is
recorded. The table shows the results.

Oil temperature/°C	Time taken/s
11	75
19	54
27	38
33	30
42	19
50	12

a) Use these results to plot a graph of time (y-axis) against temperature
  (x-axis).
b) Describe the shape of the graph and explain what it tells you about the
  way in which the viscosity of the oil changes as the temperature rises.
  A car owner wishes to change the oil in the engine. The old oil is
  removed by removing a plug at the bottom of the engine.
c) Explain why the car owner runs the engine to warm up the oil
  before removing the plug.

Q3 The diagram shows how the rate of flow of liquid through a tube can be investigated.

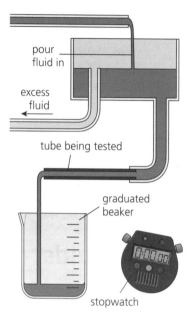

a) Explain why it is necessary to maintain a constant level of liquid in the reservoir.

The flow rate through the tube depends on the **pressure gradient**.

b) Explain the meaning of the term **pressure gradient**.

c) Write down **two** ways in which the pressure gradient can be increased.

When a liquid or gas flows through a tube the velocity is different at different parts of the tube. The arrows on the diagram represent the velocity of gas flowing in a pipe at two different parts of the pipe.

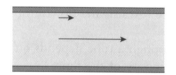

d) Complete the diagram by adding arrows to show the velocity of the gas across the cross–section of the pipe.

e) Explain why the gas near the pipe wall has the lowest velocity.

F6 Fluids and force

■ Streamlined flow offers less opposition to the flow of a fluid than turbulent flow does.

■ When a fluid flows in a pipe or past an object, the pressure is least where the speed of flow is fastest. This is known as the Bernoulli effect.

Q1 Choose the best description of turbulent flow.
  A In turbulent flow the streamlines cross each other.
  B In turbulent flow the streamlines are at fixed distances.
  C In turbulent flow the fluid flow is regular.
  D In turbulent flow the fluid flow is irregular.

Q2 Manufacturers of heavy goods vehicles often fit a metal sheet between the cab and the trailer. This metal sheet helps to maintain a streamlined flow of air past the vehicle.

a) Explain how the metal sheet helps to maintain a streamlined air flow.

   b) What advantage does a streamlined air flow have:
      i) to the driver of the vehicle?
     ii) to the owner of the vehicle?

Q3 The diagram shows the airflow around an aircraft wing.
   a) Describe how the speed of the air
      over the upper surface differs from
      that over the lower surface.
   b) Explain how this difference in air
      speeds gives the aircraft lift.
   When ice forms on the wings of an aircraft the aircraft loses lift.
   c) Suggest what effect the ice has on the airflow to cause the aircraft to
      lose lift.

Q4 When a table tennis player applies topspin to the ball as it is hit, the ball
    moves in a sharply curved path.

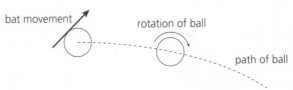

   a) Draw a diagram showing the streamlines around the ball.
   b) Explain how the air exerts a downward force on the ball.
   c) Use a diagram to explain how a footballer can cause a football to
      swerve to one side.

G Radioactivity

53–4 Radioactive emissions

■ Alpha particles consist of two neutrons and two protons. They are intensely ionising but not very penetrative.
■ Beta particles are fast-moving electrons. They also cause ionisation and are more penetrative than alpha particles.
■ Gamma rays are short-wavelength, electromagnetic radiation. They are weakly ionising and very penetrative.
■ Radioactive decay is a random process. The decay of a particular unstable nucleus cannot be predicted but, statistically, the rate of decay of a sample of radioactive material depends on the number of unstable nuclei present.
■ The half-life of a radioactive material is the average time for the number of undecayed nuclei in a sample of the material to halve.

Q1 Which type of radioactive emission:
   a) is positively charged
   b) is not deflected by magnetic fields
   c) is the most penetrative
   d) is the most intensely ionising
   e) cannot pass through cardboard
   f) does not cause a change in mass number or atomic number
   g) has the greatest mass?

Q2 Which line in the table describes the effect on the mass and atomic number when an atom emits a beta particle?

	Change in mass number	Change in atomic number
A	0	+1
B	+1	0
C	−1	+1
D	+1	−1

Q3 The table shows the results of a laboratory experiment to measure the half-life of sodium-24, an isotope used in medicine.

Time/h	0	6	12	18	24	30	36	42	48	54	60
Activity/counts per s	692	531	405	297	232	178	135	102	85	59	42

   a) Use the data to plot a graph of activity (y-axis) against time (x-axis) and draw the best smooth curve.
   b) Explain why all the points do not lie exactly on the curve.
   c) Use your graph to find the average time for the activity of the sodium-24 sample to halve.
   d) Estimate the time from the beginning of the experiment when the activity of the sample has fallen to 20 counts/s.

Q4 **a)** Explain why alpha particles are sometimes referred to as 'helium nuclei'.

A radioactive source is known to give off two types of radioactive emission.

b) Describe a test to find out which two types are being emitted.

c) Explain why alpha radiation is more intensely ionising than either beta or gamma radiation.

Q5 Molybdenum-99 is used in hospitals. It has a half-life of 67 hours and decays by beta emission to a form of technetium-99, which is also unstable and decays by gamma emission with a half-life of 6 hours.

a) Explain why the half-life of molybdenum-99 cannot be measured from a graph of the activity against time.

b) A hospital takes a delivery consisting of 800 g of molybdenum-99. Use a half-life graph to determine how much of the sample is still molybdenum-99 after: i) 24 hours ii) 48 hours.

c) After how long is the quantity of molybdenum in the sample likely to be: i) 400 g ii) 100 g?

d) Explain how the production rate of technetium-99 is affected by the decay of the molybdenum-99.

Q6 Complete the nuclear equations by writing in the mass number and atomic number where these are shown by a $\star$.

a) Thorium decays to radium be emitting an alpha particle.
$$^{228}_{90}\text{Th} \rightarrow {}^{\star}_{\star}\alpha + {}^{\star}_{\star}\text{Ra}$$

b) Cobalt decays to nickel by beta emission.
$$^{\star}_{\star}\text{Co} \rightarrow {}^{\star}_{\star}\beta + {}^{60}_{28}\text{Ni}$$

Q7 Iodine-123 and iodine-131 are both radioactive isotopes that can be used to examine the thyroid gland. Iodine-123 decays by gamma emission only and has a half-life of 13 hours. Iodine-131 emits alpha, beta and gamma radiation and has a half-life of 8 days.

a) Which of the radiations from iodine-131 could be detected outside the body?

b) Explain why a patient would have to be given a larger dose of iodine-131 than of iodine-123.

c) Explain the other disadvantages of using iodine-131.

55–6 Using radioactivity

- All living things are radioactive due to the presence of carbon-14 in the atmosphere.
- The age of a dead object can be estimated from the proportion of carbon-14 in the object or by measuring the radioactivity of the object.
- Rocks can be dated by measuring the proportions of radioactive materials and materials that form when radioactive decay occurs.
- Radioactive materials are commonly used as tracers, thickness gauges and to generate electricity.
- When choosing a radioactive isotope for a particular purpose, the half-life and type of emission need to be considered.

Q1 Radioactive carbon-14 decays by emitting beta particles with a half-life of 5730 years.

   a) Draw an activity–time graph for carbon-14, starting with an activity of 100 counts/s and using a time scale of 20 000 years.

   b) Use your graph to explain why the decay of carbon-14 cannot be used to date objects thought to be about 100 years old.

A 1g sample of new wood has an activity of 0.255 counts/s.

   c) Explain why it is difficult to measure the activity of a 1 g sample of wood.

   d) Calculate the activity of a 392 g sample of new wood.

   e) Use your graph to estimate the age of a 392 g sample of wood that has an activity of 82 counts/s.

Radiocarbon dating is not a precise method of dating objects.

   f) Explain why it is not possible to date objects precisely by measuring the amount of carbon-14 present.

Q2 The table shows some radioactive materials found in rocks, with their half-lives and the substances formed when they decay.

The age of the Earth is thought to be 4600 million years.
Rocks are dated by comparing the amount of an isotope to the amount formed when it decays.

Isotope	Substance formed	Half-life /millions of years
rubidium-87	strontium-87	49 000
thorium-232	lead-208	14 000
uranium-238	lead-206	4 500
potassium-40	argon-40	1 250
uranium-235	lead-207	704
iodine-129	xenon-129	17

   a) Explain which isotope would be most suitable for dating rocks thought to have the same age as the Earth.

A rock is found to contain thorium-232 and lead-208 in the ratio 1:3.

b) Estimate the age of the rock.

c) Explain why rocks cannot be dated by comparing the proportions of iodine-129 and xenon-129.

Q3 A sample of technetium-99 with a half-life of 6 hours has an activity of 160 counts/s. The activity of the sample 12 hours later is likely to be:
A 0 counts/s   B 40 counts/s   C 80 counts/s   D 320 counts/s.

Q4 Scalpel blades, syringes and other surgical equipment can be sterilised by radiation. They are sealed in foil or plastic before being irradiated. This ensures that they are sterile until the packet is opened.
a) Which type of radiation should be used?
b) Explain why the other types would not be suitable.
c) If you were in charge of an irradiating company, would you prefer to use an isotope with a long half-life or a short half-life? Explain your choice.

Q5 Domestic smoke detectors use a source of alpha radiation. The alpha radiation ionises air particles in an ionisation chamber, which is open to the air in the room, causing a current to pass. The alarm sounds when the current falls below its normal level. The diagram shows the main components of a smoke alarm.

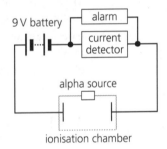

a) Explain why an alpha source, rather than a beta or gamma source, is used to ionise the air.
b) Explain why the ionisation current falls when smoke enters the ionisation chamber.
Fire prevention officers recommend that the battery in a smoke detector is changed at least once a year.
c) Explain why a failing battery could cause the alarm to sound.
Fire prevention officers also recommend that when the battery is changed all dust is removed from the smoke detector.
d) Why is this sensible advice?

Q6 When meteorites strike the surface of a planet, they may cause localised melting. This may result in the loss of substances formed by radioactive decay. Explain how dating of the rocks around a meteor crater could give information about when the meteor struck.

G1 The atom

■ Most of the mass of an atom is contained in its nucleus, a region of intense mass and positive charge.
■ The atomic number is the number of protons in a nucleus. The mass number is the total number of protons and neutrons.
■ The electrons in orbit around a nucleus can only occupy certain allowed orbits.

Q1 Evidence for the atomic nucleus comes from the scattering of alpha particles. Choose the option that is a source of alpha particles.
A cobalt-60 B carbon-14 C radon-220 D thorium-232

Q2 Describe the structure of the nucleus for the following atoms:
a) $^{9}_{4}$Be b) $^{89}_{39}$Y c) $^{162}_{66}$Dy

Q3 The diagram shows the scattering of alpha particles by gold foil.
a) Why is gold the most suitable material for showing alpha particle scattering?
b) Explain why most of the particles show little or no deviation.
c) Which of the alpha particles shown in the diagram must have experienced a repulsive force?
d) What does this repulsive force tell you about the type of charge that a nucleus has?

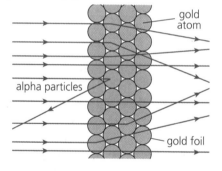

Q4 Line spectra provide evidence that electrons in orbit can only have certain amounts of energy. What these amounts are depends on the atom.
a) What is the difference between a line spectrum and a continuous spectrum?
The diagram shows the possible energy levels for an electron in orbit around a hydrogen nucleus.
b) Use the diagram to show why an electron in orbit can only absorb certain amounts of energy.
c) Use the diagram to explain what happens when an excited electron gives off electromagnetic radiation.

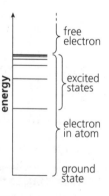

Q5 a) Explain how the colour of the light emitted when an electron loses energy depends on the the amount of energy lost.
b) Suggest how the movement of an electron between energy levels can lead to the emission of: i) infrared radiation ii) X-rays.

G2 Atomic stability

■ Electrons, positrons and quarks are fundamental particles. Protons and neutrons consist of different combinations of the 'up' and 'down' quarks.

■ The stability of a nucleus depends on its proton : neutron ratio. If this is too low it decays by β⁻ emission; too high a ratio leads to β⁺ emission.

■ Unstable nuclei with more than 82 protons decay by emitting an apha particle.

■ The energy released by nuclear fission or fusion can be calculated using the equation: $E = mc^2$

Q1 Which statement is the correct description of Einstein's mass–energy relationship?
   A Energy can be changed into mass.
   B Mass can be changed into energy.
   C Mass and energy are interchangeable.
   D Energy has mass.

Q2 The diagram shows the quarks that make up a proton and a neutron.

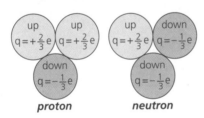

proton   **neutron**

   a) Explain how a proton changes into a neutron.
   b) Explain how a neutron changes into a proton.

Q3 Nuclei with less than 20 protons are stable if the proton : neutron ratio is 1:1.
   a) Explain why $^{14}_{6}C$ is unstable.
   b) Describe how a $^{14}_{6}C$ nucleus can change to a stable nucleus by emitting a beta particle.
   c) Write an equation for the decay of $^{14}_{6}C$.
   d) Which would you expect to have the greater mass, the original nucleus or the products of the decay? Explain why this is.

Q4 $^{11}_{6}C$ decays to boron, symbol B, by β⁺ emission.
   a) Write the decay equation.
   b) Calculate the proton : neutron ratio of the carbon and the boron.
   c) Show that the proton : neutron ratio becomes closer to 1:1 when the carbon nucleus changes into a nucleus of boron.

Q5 $^{215}_{85}At$ is an isotope of astatine that decays by alpha emission to an isotope of bismuth, symbol Bi.

a) Write the decay equation.

b) Calculate the proton : neutron ratio for the astatine and the bismuth and describe how it changes when the astatine decays into bismuth.

c) Use the following information to calculate the difference in mass between astatine and the decay products.

Particle	Mass/u
astatine nucleus	214.95616
bismuth nucleus	210.94579
helium nucleus	4.00060

d) Calculate the energy released when astatine decays to bismuth and an alpha particle.

$$1\,u = 1.661 \times 10^{-27}\,kg$$
$$c = 3.00 \times 10^8\,m/s.$$

e) Explain what happens to the energy released when the astatine decays.

Review questions

A Electricity, electronics and magnetism *(Units 1–16, A1–A6)*

Q1 The diagram shows how a variable resistor can be used to control the brightness of a lamp. The resistance of the variable resistor can be set in the range $0\,\Omega$ (for maximum brightness) to $600\,\Omega$ (when the lamp is dim). The lamp filament has a resistance of $1000\,\Omega$ when operating at its maximum brightness.

a) Calculate the current in the circuit when the lamp is at its maximum brightness.

b) Calculate the power of the lamp at its maximum brightness.

When the variable resistor is adjusted to make the lamp dim, the voltage across the lamp filament is 120 V.

c) Write down the voltage across the variable resistor when the lamp is dim.

d) Calculate the current in the circuit when the lamp is dim.

e) Calculate the power of the lamp when it is dim.

f) Explain why the variable resistor may become hot when the lamp is dim but stays cool when the lamp is bright.

Q2 Televisions use both step-up and step-down transformers to increase and decrease the size of the mains voltage.

a) Draw and label a diagram of a transformer.

b) Describe the difference in the construction of a step-up and a step-down transformer.

c) Explain why a step-up transformer cannot be used to change the 12 V d.c. from a car battery into 240 V a.c.

A transformer used in a battery charger has an input voltage of 240 V and an output voltage of 16 V. The primary coil has 1500 turns of wire.

d) Calculate the number of turns of wire on the secondary coil.

e) Calculate the current in the secondary coil when the current in the primary coil is 0.5 A.

B Forces and motion *(Units 17–26, B1–B5)*

Q1 Here is a speed–time graph.

a) Calculate the distance travelled for each of the sections labelled **A, B, C** and **D**.

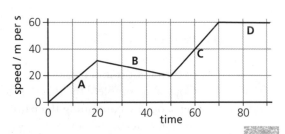

97

b) Calculate the average speed in the 90 s shown on the graph.

c) Which section shows the greatest acceleration? Explain how you can tell.

d) Calculate the value of this acceleration.

Q2 A car of mass 850 kg is travelling at 12.5 m/s on a level road. The car brakes with uniform deceleration and comes to a halt after 4.1 s.

a) Calculate the deceleration (negative acceleration) of the car.

b) Calculate the size of the braking force needed to cause this deceleration.

c) How far does the car travel during braking?

d) Explain how the braking distance of a car depends on its speed.

C Waves *(Units 27–38, C1–C7)*

Q1 The diagram shows a transverse wave travelling along a rope.

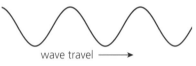

wave travel ⟶

a) Describe the movement of each part of the rope as the wave travels along it.

b) On a copy of the diagram, mark with an 'a' a distance which is equal to the amplitude of the wave.

c) Mark with a 'λ' a distance which is equal to one wavelength of the wave. When the frequency of the wave is 1.5 Hz it has a wavelength of 7.5 m.

d) Calculate the speed of the wave along the rope.

Q2 The table shows some uses of waves from different parts of the electromagnetic spectrum. Complete the table by writing in a property of each wave that makes it suitable for the given use. The first one has been done for you.

Type of radiation	Use	Property that makes it suitable for that use
gamma rays	sterilising medical equipment	kills bacteria
X-rays	examining bones for damage	
light	vision	
microwaves	cooking	
infrared	infrared cameras that can 'see' in the dark	
ultraviolet	sun beds	
radio	communication	

Q3 Periscopes use either mirrors or prisms to turn light round corners. Copy and complete the diagram of a periscope by continuing the paths of the light rays as they enter the eye.

D The Earth and its place in the Universe *(Units 39–42, D1)*

Q1 The table gives some data about the five outer planets.

Planet	Radius/km	Mass (Earth = 1)	Density/g per cm³	Surface gravitational field strength/ N per kg	Surface temperature/°C	Radius of orbit (Earth = 1)
Jupiter	71 000	318	1.33	23	−150	5.2
Saturn	60 000	95	0.71	8.9	−180	9.5
Uranus	25 500	15	1.24	8.7	−215	19.1
Neptune	24 800	17	1.67	11	−220	30
Pluto	1 120	0.025	1.95	0.72	−225	39.5

a) Write down two reasons why Pluto is the odd one out.

The gravitational field strength on Saturn is similar to that on Uranus, although Saturn is a more massive planet.

b) Suggest a reason for this.

c) Write down two reasons why, of the planets shown in the table, Jupiter has the shortest year.

d) Describe and explain the pattern in surface temperature of the planets.

e) What other factors could affect the surface temperature of a planet?

Q2 The Universe is thought to have started with an enormous explosion. The first substances that formed after the explosion were hydrogen and helium. Heavier elements were later formed in stars.

a) Suggest how the heavier elements could have formed.

b) Explain why our Solar System could not have been formed at the same time as the first stars in the Universe.

One theory about the origin of the Solar System is that it was formed from a spinning cloud of dust that was part of the remains of an exploding supernova.

c) Describe how this theory explains the fact that the innermost planets are denser than the outer planets.

The Universe is still expanding but the rate of expansion may be decreasing.

d) Suggest why the rate of expansion may be decreasing.

e) Explain how the expansion of the Universe supports the theory that it started as a single explosion.

E Energy *(Units 43–51)*

Q1 Explain the following.

a) The cooling rate of a hot drink is reduced when it is in a container fitted with a lid.

b) Metal foil containers provide good insulation for hot take-away food.

c) Some householders put kitchen foil on the wall behind a central heating radiator.

Q2 The diagram shows the driving force acting on a car which is travelling at a constant speed of 15 m/s.

800 N

a) How much work is done by the driving force in 10 s?

b) Calculate the power output of the car engine and drive mechanism.

c) The efficiency of the car is 0.25. Use the formula:

efficiency = useful power output ÷ total power input

to calculate the power input to the car engine.

d) Compare the kinetic energy of an 800 kg car travelling at 15 m/s with that of a similar car travelling at 30 m/s.

Both cars are stopped using a braking force of 6000 N.

e) Compare the braking distances for the two cars and explain the pattern in your answer.

F Molecular physics *(Units 52, F1–F6)*

Q1 A pressurised container contains carbon dioxide gas at a pressure of 1 200 000 Pa. The surface area of the inner walls of the container is 0.03 m^2.

a) Calculate the force on the walls of the container due to the gas pressure.

b) Explain how the gas particles exert such a large pressure.

c) Describe and explain the effect on the gas pressure if the temperature of the gas decreases.

Gas cylinders are coloured according to the gas that they contain. Carbon dioxide cylinders are black.

d) What advice would you give to a manufacturer who stores cylinders of carbon dioxide outside?

Q2 a) Explain how Brownian motion and diffusion support the theory that matter is made up of moving particles.

b) Describe the movement of the particles in:

i) a solid   ii) a liquid   iii) a gas.

c) Explain why it is not possible to predict the movement of an individual gas particle.

'The pressure of a gas is proportional to its temperature'.

d) Under what circumstances do gases behave in this way?

G Radioactivity *(Units 53–56, G1–G2)*

Q1 a) Describe the nature of the three principal radioactive emissions: alpha
particles, beta particles and gamma rays.

    b) Which of the three can be deflected by:

      i) electric fields

      ii) magnetic fields?

    c) The diagram shows a film badge, a device used
to monitor the amount of radiation that a worker
is exposed to. Explain which type of radiation
could be detected by each part of the film.

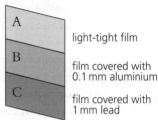

light-tight film

film covered with
0.1 mm aluminium

film covered with
1 mm lead

Q2 Over a period of one hour, ten readings are taken of the activity of a
20 g sample of new wood. The results are shown in the table.

Reading	1	2	3	4	5	6	7	8	9	10
Activity/counts per minute	300	297	305	310	302	315	307	303	311	310

    a) Explain why the number of counts in one minute is measured rather
than the number of counts in one second.

    b) Suggest why a 20 g sample is likely to give more reliable results than a
1 g sample.

The isotope responsible for the radioactivity, carbon–14, has a half-life of
5730 years.

    c) Explain why the results do not show a downward trend.

    d) Explain why there is variation in the results obtained.

    e) Calculate a value for the average activity in counts/s.

    f) Estimate the activity of a similar sample of the wood from a tree that
died 10 000 years ago.

Reference section

Glossary

A **Absolute zero** The lowest possible temperature.

Acceleration Increase in velocity (or speed) per second.

Air resistance The force from the air that acts in the opposite direction to motion.

Alpha particle A particle consisting of two neutrons and two protons emitted from a decaying nucleus.

Ammeter Instrument that measures electric current.

Ampere The unit of electric current.

Amplitude Maximum displacement of a wave from the undisturbed position.

Amplitude modulation (AM) A method of transmitting information by changing the amplitude of a radio wave.

Angle of incidence The angle between light hitting a surface and the normal line.

Angle of reflection The angle between light hitting a surface and the normal line.

Angle of refraction The angle between light that has passed through a surface and the normal line.

Armature Rotating part of an electric motor.

Asteroid Piece of rock found in the asteroid belt, between Mars and Jupiter.

Atomic number The number of protons in the nucleus of an atom.

B **Background radiation** Radiation from the ground, the atmosphere, our surroundings and space that is present all the time.

Bernoulli's principle A principle that relates the speed of fluid flow to changes in pressure.

Beta particle Particle emitted from a decaying nucleus consisting of an electron.

Big bang Theory that the Universe start with a tremendous explosion.

Bimetallic strip Device consisting of tw different metals joined together in suc way that it changes shape when the temperature changes.

Bistable A circuit that can maintain eith of two possible output states.

Boyle's law Describes the relationship between the pressure and the volume of a gas.

Braking distance The distance a vehicl travels while braking to a halt.

Brownian motion The erratic motion small particles suspended in a fluid.

C **Capacitor** Device that stores charg

Cathode ray oscilloscope Used to disp the variation of a voltage with time.

Celsius A temperature scale derived fron the kelvin scale. Found by adding 273 the kelvin temperature.

Centre of mass The point on an object that its weight acts from.

Circuit breaker Device that cuts off the electricity supply if a fault develops.

Colour filter Allows some colours of light to pass through, and absorbs other colours.

Compass Small pivoted magnet that po towards magnetic North.

Concave The shape of a lens that is thin in the middle than on the outside.

Conduction A mechanism of transfer of heat or electricity.

Conservation of momentum A principle that the total momentum of a system remains constant.

Constructive interference When two, or more waves interfere to give an increased amplitude.

Convection Movement of air currents due to differences in density.

Convex The shape of a lens that is thicker in the middle than on the outside.

Coulomb The unit of electric charge.

Crumple zone The part of a vehicle designed to protect passengers by absorbing the energy of an impact as it crumples.

Crust The outer layer of the Earth.

Current A flow of electric charge.

D **Density** The mass of each cubic centimetre of a material. It has units of kg/m or g/cm.

Destructive interference Two or more waves interfere to give a reduced amplitude.

Diffraction The spreading out of a wave as it passes through an opening, or by the edge of an obstacle.

Diffusion The spreading out of a fluid due to particle motion.

Diode A device that allows electric current to pass in one direction only.

Diode laser A diode that emits electromagnetic radiation of one wavelength when it is conducting.

Displacement Is the change of position of an object.

Domain A region of magnetised material.

Doppler effect The change in apparent wavelength and frequency of light or sound due to movement of an object or an observer.

Double insulation Where the casing of an electrical device is insulated as well as the wires.

Dynamo A device for generating electricity, consisting of a magnet that rotates inside a coil of wire.

E **Earth wire** A safety wire, connecting the metal case of an appliance to the earth.

Echo A reflection of a sound.

Efficiency The proportion of energy input that is transferred to a useful output.

Elastic The property of regaining shape after deformation.

Elastic limit The maximum force that can be applied to an object while it remains elastic.

Electromagnet A magnet whose magnetic field is caused by a current passing in a coil of wire.

Electromagnetic induction Producing a voltage or current in a conductor due to the change of a magnetic field.

Electromagnetic spectrum The family of electromagnetic waves arranged in order of frequency.

Electromagnetic wave A wave consisting of oscillating electric and magnetic fields at right angles to each other.

Electron A fundamental particle that orbits the nucleus in an atom. It is a negatively charged particle and is responsible for electrical conduction in metals.

Electrostatic precipitator Used to remove ash from power station smoke.

Endoscope A medical device that uses optical fibres for seeing inside the body.

Energy The ability to do work, e.g. cause motion.

Energy level A possible orbit of an electron around a nucleus.

Glossary

Evaporation The process by which a liquid changes to a vapour, due to particles leaving the surface of the liquid. This happens at temperatures below the boiling point but is fastest when the liquid is boiling.

F **Feedback** Part of the output of an electronic system that returns to the input.

Filament lamp A lamp that gives out light from a heated filament.

Fission The splitting of an atomic nucleus into smaller atoms, with the release of neutrons and energy.

Fluid A liquid or a gas.

Fluorescent lamp A lamp that gives out light from an ionised gas.

Focal length The distance from the centre of a lens to the principal focus.

Free-fall Vertical motion with no resistive forces acting.

Frequency modulation (FM) A method of transmitting information by changing the frequency of a radio wave.

Friction A force that opposes objects sliding over or past each other.

Fuse A thin wire that melts to cut off the supply to a circuit when the current exceeds a stated value. Thus the fuse acts as a safety device.

Fusion Process by which large nuclei are formed when smaller nuclei merge.

G **Galaxy** A collection of stars held together by gravitational forces.

Gamma ray Short wavelength electromagnetic radiation emitted from a nucleus.

Gas equation Describes the relationship between the pressure, volume and temperature of a gas.

Geiger-Müller tube A detector of radioactivity and radiation.

Generator Generates electricity by an electromagnet spinning inside a coil of wire.

Geostationary A satellite orbit where a satellite remains in the same position relative to the Earth.

Gravitational force An attractive force between any two objects that have mass.

Ground wave A wave that follows the Earth's curvature.

H **Half-life** The average time for the number of radioactive atoms to fall to half the original number.

Harmonic A whole-number multiple of the natural frequency.

Hertz The unit of frequency.

Hooke's law Describes the behaviour of some materials when they are deformed.

Hydraulic Uses liquids to transmit pressure.

I **Impulse** The product of the size of a force and the time for which it acts.

Infrared Electromagnetic radiation given out by all objects.

Insulation Reduces the flow of heat, or prevents the flow of charge.

Interference Two or more waves combine to give a total displacement equal to the sum of the individual displacements.

Isotope Atoms with the same atomic number, but different mass numbers.

J **Joule** The unit of work and energy.

Joulemeter Measures energy transfer from electricity.

K **Kelvin** The absolute scale of temperature.

Kilowatt-hour The domestic unit of energy from electricity.
Kinetic energy Energy due to the movement of an object.

L **Latch** A device that retains its output when the input has been removed.
Left-hand rule Used to predict the direction of motion of the coil of an electric motor.
Lever A device for changing the size of a force or the movement caused by a force.
Light-dependent resistor An electronic component whose resistance depends on its illumination.
Limit of proportionality The force at which an object stops following Hooke's law.
Linear expansivity The fractional change in length for each degree change in temperature.
Live wire The wire that supplies energy to an electrical device.
Logic gate A digital electronic device used for decision-making.
Long sight A condition where the eye cannot focus near objects.
Longitudinal A wave in which the vibrations are parallel to the direction of motion.
Loudspeaker Device that produces sound when an alternating current passes in it.
Lubricant Prevents surfaces from rubbing together.

M **Magnetic field** A region where a magnetic force acts.
Mantle The part of the Earth between the core and the crust.
Mass number The total number of neutrons and protons in the nucleus of an atom.

Microphone Device that produces an electrical representation of a sound.
Microwave Short wavelength radio wave used in cooking, relaying telephone conversations, and radio and television.
Milky Way The galaxy containing our Sun.
Moment The turning effect of a force.
Momentum The product of mass and velocity.

N **National grid** The network of cables and transformers that distributes electricity around the country.
Natural frequency The frequency of vibration of an object that is struck.
Nebula A cloud of gas and dust.
Neutral wire The return wire for electric current.
Normal line A line drawn at right angles to a surface.

O **Optical fibre** A glass or plastic fibre that transmits light.
Orbit The path of an object that goes around another object.
Oscillation A vibration or to-and-fro motion.

P **Parallel circuit** A circuit containing more than one current path.
Path difference The difference in the distances travelled by two waves, expressed as a number of wavelengths.
Photodiode A diode that only conducts when it is illuminated by light or other electromagnetic radiation.
Pivot A point that objects turn around.
Planet A large body that orbits a Sun.
Plastic An object that is permanently deformed when a force is applied.
Positron A fundamental particle with the same mass as an electron but the opposite charge.

Glossary

Potential divider An arrangement of two resistors in series that divides a voltage into two parts.

Potential energy Energy due to position relative to the surface of the Earth.

Power The rate of energy transfer or doing work.

Pressure law Describes the relationship between the pressure of a gas and its kelvin temperature.

Pressure The force per unit area. Pressure is measured in N/m^2 or Pa.

Primary colour A colour that cannot be created by mixing other colours of light.

Principal focus The point where a lens focuses a beam of parallel light.

Processor The part of an electronic system that handles information.

Projectile An object travelling horizontally as well as vertically.

Q **Quark** A fundamental particle.

R **Radioactivity** Emissions by a nucleus changing to a more stable state.

Radio wave Long-wavelength electromagnetic wave.

Random With no set order or pattern.

Reaction time The time lapse between an event and a person reacting to it

Real image An image that can be projected on a screen.

Recoil The backwards movement of an object that fires a projectile.

Red shift The change in frequency of light caused by an object moving away from an observer.

Refraction The change in speed of a wave due to a change in the medium that the wave is travelling through.

Refractive index The ratio of the speed of light in a material to the speed of light in a vacuum.

Relay An electromagnetic switch.

Resistance The opposition to charge flow provided by a resistor.

Resonance A large-amplitude vibration at the natural frequency caused by a forced vibration at that frequency.

Resultant force The overall force when two or more forces act on an object.

Reverberation A sound continuing to be heard due to reflections from the walls and surfaces of a room.

S **Secondary colour** One that can be made by mixing light of two primary colours.

Seismic wave A wave that travels through the Earth.

Seismometer A device for recording seismic waves.

Series circuit A circuit in which there is only one current path.

Short sight A condition where the eye cannot focus distant objects.

Sky wave A wave that is reflected by the ionosphere.

Space wave A wave that only travels in straight lines.

Specific heat capacity The energy transfer when 1 kg of material changes temperature by one degree.

Specific latent heat The energy transfer when 1 kg of material changes state without a change in temperature.

Speed The distance travelled per second.

Star A large mass that gives out light due to heating caused by nuclear fusion.

Stiffness How difficult it is to deform an object.

Stopping distance The total distance travelled by a vehicle between an event happening and the vehicle coming to rest.

Streamlined flow A smooth flow of fluid round an object.

Supernova A star shining very brightly at the end of its main sequence.

T **Thermistor** A component whose resistance depends on its temperature.

Thinking distance The distance travelled by a vehicle during the driver's reaction time.

Timbre The quality of a musical sound made by an instrument.

Total internal reflection (TIR) All the light meeting the boundary between two transparent substances is reflected.

Tracer A radioactive substance used to track the path of a fluid.

Transformer A device for changing the size of an alternating voltage.

Transistor An electronic device used for switching and amplification.

Transverse A wave motion where the vibrations are at right angles to the direction of wave travel.

Turbulent flow An irregular flow of fluid around an object.

Turning effect The effect a force has in causing rotation.

U **Ultrasound** Sound waves that have a frequency above the range of human hearing.

Ultraviolet Electromagnetic wave with a wavelength shorter than that of light.

Universe Everything that exists.

V **Variable resistor** A component whose resistance can be changed, usually using a slider or a knob.

Velocity The speed and direction of a moving object.

Vibration An oscillation or to-and-fro motion.

Virtual image An image that cannot be projected onto a screen.

Viscosity Describes the ability of a fluid to flow.

Volt The unit of voltage or potential difference.

Voltmeter An instrument for measuring voltage or potential difference.

W **Watt** The unit of power.

Wavelength The length of one cycle of a wave motion.

Weight The force due to the gravitational pull on an object.

Work Work is done when a force causes motion. It is always accompanied by an energy transfer.

X **X-ray** Short-wavelength electromagnetic radiation that penetrates flesh and is partially absorbed by bone.

Formulae you should know

Here is a list of formulae that you may need to use in answering physics questions. Note that these formulae will not be given to you either on the examination paper or on a separate formula sheet.

For foundation tier papers	
voltage = current × resistance	$V = IR$
power = voltage × current	$P = VI$
average speed = distance ÷ time	$v = \dfrac{s}{t}$
acceleration = increase in velocity ÷ time	$a = \dfrac{v_2 - v_1}{t}$
pressure = force ÷ area	$P = \dfrac{F}{A}$
work done = energy transfer = force × distance moved in its own direction	$W = Fd$

In addition, for higher tier papers	
force = mass × acceleration	$F = ma$
current = charge flow ÷ time	$I = \dfrac{Q}{t}$
for a transformer: $\dfrac{\text{primary voltage}}{\text{secondary voltage}} = \dfrac{\text{number of primary turns}}{\text{number of secondary turns}}$	$\dfrac{V_p}{V_s} = \dfrac{N_p}{N_s}$
wave speed = frequency × wavelength	$v = f\lambda$

Physical quantities and their units

Physical quantity		Unit	
name	symbol	name	symbol
acceleration	a	metres per second in one second	m/s² or ms⁻²
charge	Q	coulomb	C
current	I	ampere	A
distance	s	metre	m
energy	E	joule	J
force	F	newton	N
frequency	f	hertz	Hz
mass	m	kilogram	kg
power	P	watt	W
pressure	P	pascal	Pa or N/m²
resistance	R	ohm	Ω
speed, velocity	v	metres per second	m/s or ms⁻¹
temperature	t	degree Celsius	°C
time	t	second	s
voltage	V	volt	V
wavelength	λ	metre	m
work	W	joule	J